REVERSE ENGINEERING

First published in 2022
by Scratch Books Ltd.
London

This is an anthology of fiction. All characters,
organisations, and events portrayed in each
story are either products of each author's
imagination or are used fictitiously.

Printed and bound in Great Britain by Clays Ltd,
Elcograf S.p.A.

MIX
Paper from
responsible sources
FSC® C018072

FSC
www.fsc.org

ISBN Paperback 978-1-7398301-0-6
eBook 978-1-7398301-1-3

Contents

Introduction

I magine writing a perfect short story. Not just a good story... a perfect one. It must be possible: the only thing the great short stories have in common is how close they come to perfection. And though this might be overreaching, it's true that short stories are judged by simple criteria; while there are hundreds of different ways a novel might succeed or fail, a story just has to be brilliant. Which, for its writers, is liberating and daunting and endlessly intriguing.

For example, how would you attempt to write something brilliant? How would you *know* if you had achieved it? Because they are so various, one amazing story is only a minute piece of the map; we would need an author to send back reports of their progress for us to follow them.

In maybe the earliest piece specifically on short story craft, Edgar Allan Poe wrote that: 'the unity of effect or impression is a point of the greatest importance... without unity of impression, the deepest effects cannot be brought about.'[1]

Fifty years later, Robert Louis Stevenson went further: 'I never use an effect when I can help it, unless it prepares the effects that are to follow... the body and end of a short story is bone of the bone and blood of the blood of the beginning.'[2]

Emboldened by the possibility of formal rules, the twentieth century saw a great deal of investigation into the short story, hale narratologists chasing it flapping across lawns, to later splay, pin and prod it in lecture halls. What is vital, they said, is its use of revelation, its use of tone, its mystery, its intensity, the presence of a debunking rhythm, an objective correlative, a narrative-matrix.

Some sought aphorisms to understand the short story as the younger cousin of the novel: *where the novel is _____, the short story is _____*, while others hoped to glimpse its essence within the short stories of the greats. On Raymond Carver's wall was Chekhov's 'and suddenly everything became clear to him.' But what about Carver's own 'it was like nothing else in my life up to now'? Or Alice Munro's 'something not startling until you think of trying to tell it'?[3]

Or, if there are family ties that connect all short story writing, perhaps they come from the nature of its readership.

There's a maxim in publishing that nobody reads short stories. The truth is maybe more nuanced: nobody needing the solace of a novel reads short stories. Short story readers are emotionally eloquent enough not to need consolation from life in all its heart-aching richness. Perhaps something you could also say is true of short stories...

But stories cannot be reduced in any of these ways. Such is its meeting of content and form, maybe a story cannot be expressed in any other way than by itself.

Stories are also too exceptional for any of these generalisations. There is no single landmass all these different directions lead to. The realm of the short story is a perennial newfoundland. We can only know how each one is come to.

The aim of this book is to find out from a writer how they arrived at *their* story. What were their decisions, their tendencies, their inclinations? Navigating the dark seas of inspiration, this book hopes to understand what filled their sails, what becalmed them (a painted pen above a painted notebook), when did they turn, when did they press on. Understanding writers' craft is less like a nautical map than learning to read the stars – it's not important knowing the route if the purpose of the voyage is to get lost.

Introduction

The stories in this anthology have nothing in common that I am aware of, except maybe all examples of the same vivacious diversity. Which is something I hoped to explore in the interviews; where some questions ask about individual choices the writer made, other questions – about openings, endings, inspiration, craft – I try to put to all authors.

Where the interviews in this book aim to find answers, the stories in this book merely ask questions – if short stories answered all the questions, we wouldn't have the same need of them.

[1] First published in his review of Hawthorne's Twice-Told Tales in the April 1842 issue of Graham's Magazine. Available to read in full on the Comma Press website.

[2] Taken from his Vailima letters to Sidney Colvin 1890 – 1894. Available to read at Project Gutenberg.

[3] This last from the title story from Munro's collection Open Secrets – suggested by Professor Emerita in Short Fiction, Ailsa Cox.

The Crossing

by Chris Power

Descending from Hawkridge, Ann and Jim came to the River Barle and what was marked on their map as a ford. The path ran to the water's edge and continued on the opposite bank some way downstream. The river wasn't more than thirty feet wide at this point, and the tea-coloured water didn't look deep, but it was impossible to go straight across and climb the opposite bank: a split-rail fence ran close to the water, with a barrier of alders and sedge crowded behind it. They needed to wade downstream to the continuation of the path. The river was moving rapidly, noisily sloshing over the jumbled rocks of its bed. Jim pointed out they were carrying everything they had brought with them for four days' hiking, and they didn't want to risk getting it soaked, did they? It was late September, and the first chill of autumn veined the air.

Ann was warmed now by a day's walking, but she remembered how frigid it had been when they left Dulverton early that morning. They woke before dawn, clutching each other tightly in the warm centre of the bed. The storage heater they fiddled with the previous evening had proved utterly ineffective: everything beyond their bodies lay frozen. They had only met a few weeks before, and Ann giggled nervously when she slipped out of bed and trotted, naked in the blue half-light, to the bathroom. She had lifted her feet exaggeratedly high and yelped at the floor's scathing coldness.

'We can go around,' she said, reading the map, 'but it's all the way back to that farmhouse.'

'Where those dogs were?'

She nodded.

'Miles back,' Jim said. He started taking off his boots. 'I'll go in without my pack first. See how slippery it is.' He stepped into the water, arms held out for balance. He sucked air through clenched teeth. 'Freezing,' he said.

Ann watched the river water wrinkle at his ankles, then his shins, then his knees. It darkened the folds of his trousers and pushed up to his thighs. He slipped, but recovered his balance.

'I'm all right, I'm all right,' he said hurriedly. He sounded irritated, Ann thought. She watched him stop to survey.

'Looks like it gets deeper ahead,' he said, turning; then he reeled backwards. His arms thrashed and his hands grasped the air as he went over. His hand found a rock in the water and he froze in position, one side of his torso submerged.

'Oh!' Ann cried.

Still frozen in place, he looked back at her. His eyes were wide with surprise. His position made Ann think of a breakdancer mid-move, and she smiled.

'What's funny?' he said.

She laughed, thinking he wasn't serious.

'Your wounded pride.'

Back on the riverbank Jim took off his fleece and T-shirt and wrung them out.

Ann watched as he jumped up and down to warm himself, admiring the bullish curve of his chest. 'I still think we can make it,' he said. 'Just need to be careful.'

She eyed the water dubiously. 'You said it gets deeper. I'll be in up to my waist at least.'

Rolling a cigarette, Jim shrugged agreement. He looked past her, back up the hill. 'Maybe the cavalry's arrived,' he said.

The Crossing

Ann turned and saw a man and a woman wearing matching red fleeces and black canvas trousers moving fast, their walking poles striking the ground with every step.

They were called John and Christine, and Ann guessed they were around fifty. They had the ruddy look of people who spent every weekend exposed to the elements. Jim explained about the map and the ford.

'Maps,' John said, with happy derision.

'We're not sure about it,' Ann said. 'Don't want our stuff getting drenched.' She felt this was too flimsy a reason for people like Christine and John, and was irritated that she had been the one to voice Jim's concern.

'What do you think?' Christine said to John.

'I'm not going back up that hill,' he said, grinning. 'No chance.'

'Well,' Christine said, looking between Ann and Jim, 'shall we all go together?'

'Yes!' Ann said with enthusiasm, masking the disappointment she felt that they wouldn't be crossing the river alone: it would be a lesser achievement now. She reached for Jim's arm. 'Will you be all right? Your pack's much heavier than mine.'

'Course I will,' said Jim, moving his arm away from her and adjusting the straps of his backpack, his eyes fixed on the ground. He jogged his pack up and down on his shoulders to straighten it.

They bagged their shoes and socks and rolled up their trouser legs. The mud of the riverbank was burningly cold against Ann's feet. Christine and John went in, ploughing through the water at speed. Jim stepped into the water carefully. When he was about halfway across Ann followed him, the first shock of the cold leaving her frozen in place.

The water's flow wasn't strong enough to tug, but some of the stones on the riverbed were sharp, and others slick with moss. Ann felt her feet slide a little beneath her. It was like walking on seaweed. She waited as Jim tested his footing. 'Bit tricky here,' he muttered over his shoulder.

'Move a little faster if you can, Jim,' she said. 'It'll be harder when your feet get numb.' She looked up at the grey sky. A bird call, a series of digital-sounding beeps, travelled over the water and received a reply from the opposite bank.

Up ahead, she saw Christine passing one of her poles back to Jim. John was on the far bank, fifteen feet down stream. 'You want this?' he called, holding a pole in the air.

'Yes please!' Ann said. John launched it into the air. To catch it she had to lean over so far that she almost fell. She yanked her body upright, willing herself to stay standing. Jim laughed; John and Christine clapped.

'Nice catch,' Jim said. Pleased with herself, Ann pumped the air with the pole. Now the crossing was simple. Beyond the river, in a field of close-cropped pasture, Ann and Jim took off their packs and sat on grass that seemed to radiate heat after the coldness of the water.

'Where are you guys headed?' Jim asked.

'Nepal,' John and Christine said, almost in unison. 'In a few weeks, that is,' John said. 'Just Winsford for now.'

'We're getting our walking legs into shape,' Christine said.

'Nepal, fantastic!' said Ann. She thought of how they had plunged into the water and saw them dropping, in matching outfits, into a crevasse.

The two couples set off in opposite directions. 'Make sure you take those poles with you,' Jim called after them, 'they're lifesavers.'

The walking that day had been all climbs and descents. It was a pleasure now to amble through flat pasture beside the chattering river. The clouds seemed to be thinning, and Ann felt warm after being immersed in the cold water. The strangled-sounding croaks of cock pheasants came from clumps of bilberry and heather edging the pasture. From time to time the birds' plump copper bodies could be seen scurrying from one patch of cover to another.

'Only a week till the shooting season starts,' Jim said.

'I didn't know you shot,' said Ann.

'I don't much,' Jim said.

'What do you shoot? Not animals, right?'

Jim paused and looked at her. 'No,' he said.

'Would you shoot an animal?'

He looked away. 'No,' he said.

He was lying. She knew he was lying. Several times, in the weeks since she met him, Ann had thought Jim was telling her what she wanted to hear. Even before she agreed to this weekend away the trait had been irritating her. Now she regretted having come. She had wanted to sleep with him as soon as she saw him, leaning against the kitchen counter at a party in a big, dilapidated house in Chalk Farm. And she had slept with him, but now she wished she had left it at that.

The sky continued to lighten. Wisps of cloud blew across a moon-white sun. A walking trip had been Jim's idea, and Ann had loved the thought of exploring a landscape, but she saw now that for him the pleasure lay in reaching a goal – twelve miles in a day, tick – while she was more interested in seeing things she might otherwise not. Earlier in the day, having established that Jim didn't know the names of most trees and flowers, she had tried to teach him some as they walked – hazel, alder, balsam – but it soon became clear he wasn't interested. Now she did it obstinately, pointing to a clump of clover-like leaves beside a kissing gate. 'Wood sorrel,' she said.

Jim barely looked where she had pointed. He pushed the gate open for her. Earlier in the day they had made an event of these gates, puckering their lips exaggeratedly. On a quiet woodland path just before the climb up to Hawkridge, their kiss had developed into something more serious as they passed through the gate – she was here anyway, she thought, and he was sexy even if he was annoying. Ann had backed against a tree, tugging Jim after her. She was gripping his erection through his trousers when she heard the clinking of camping gear, and they were still arranging themselves when a pair of older, silver-haired walkers strode past, packs swaying. Breezily they said hello, then fell laughing against each other after the strangers had passed. Now, angry at the lie, Ann still lifted her face as they passed through the gate but kept her mouth closed against the thrust of Jim's tongue. She made a joke of it. 'Wait till we're in Withypool,' she said, swatting his chest.

'Ah, Withypool,' Jim said with mock awe, 'the Paris of Somerset.'

They continued moving upriver. The rushing water flashed blackly beside them. Jim was looking at something as they passed, and Ann turned to see a short metal ladder and a small cage affixed to the side of an oak.

'For hunting?' she said.

'Guess so,' he said.

Ann shook her head. Looking away, towards the water, she saw an uneven path of stepping stones running across the river. They stood from its surface like the vertebrae of a giant animal. 'Look!' she said. She reached into the thigh pocket of Jim's combat trousers for the map. She spread the map on the ground and traced her finger across it. Withypool lay on the other side of a steep ridge. 'If we cut across,' she said, 'we'll avoid the climb completely.'

Jim crouched down beside the river, his back to Ann.

'Jim, what d'you think? It knocks about a mile off. We could be in Withypool in less than half an hour.'

He still didn't answer. Ann stood and walked over to him. The river was deeper here, and running fast. The large, irregularly shaped stones standing proud of the water were a mottled grey, their corners furred with dark green moss. The ones that sat lower in the flow were black and glossy like a killer whale's skin.

An arrow of sun pierced the cloud and struck the running water, sending sparks skidding over its surface. It turned the foam fringing the stones gold, and for a moment the water became too brilliant to look at. It roared like a crowd in Ann's ears. Jim stood.

'Well?' Ann said, shrugging. 'Man or mouse?'

Jim smiled at her and looked away. 'Nah,' he said. 'Let's stick to the plan.'

'Really?' said Ann. She kept her voice light, but disappointment yawned in her. 'Could be fun?' she said.

'Yeah.' Jim sounded unconvinced. 'I think we had our fun for the day back there. It looks easy, I know, but the water's deeper here. One slip and it's goodbye dry gear. Tomorrow'd be a joke in wet clothes.' He picked up the map and folded it away as he started walking, then turned around and took a few steps backwards. 'Come on,' he said, 'Guinness on me when we get there.'

Ann forced a smile and gave him a thumbs up. She looked from one stepping stone to the next, to a cluster of white flowers nodding just above the water on the far bank. Seventeen stones. She threw a handful of plucked grass into the current and watched as the blades were snatched rapidly away.

Jim was already a good distance ahead, ascending the ridge; above him a group of sheep moved away at his approach. Keep going, you arsehole, Ann thought. She climbed after him. She wanted to be on her own, but didn't know how Jim would react if she crossed the river without him. She couldn't be bothered dealing with his anger, or worse, his sulking. At the top of the field, she turned just as the sun broke out again. The river ran white with light. She saw herself halfway across it, jumping from stone to stone towards the bright, empty fields beyond.

The path climbed into a wood. Ann stepped up old stone steps with risers more than a foot tall. Rivulets streaked the steep hillside. Some of them held no more than a trickle, while in others the water gushed down to join the river that now lay far below. Ann couldn't see Jim, but she could smell his acrid tobacco smoke on the air. She swatted the air and rubbed her eyes. She felt tired, and angry with herself for being here at all. Why did she always prolong things when she knew they weren't going to work? She fought an urge to stop walking and lie down beside the path. She passed another field of sheep, their coats marked with sprays of blue dye. Most of them were shambling away from the fence: Jim's living wake. Only one sheep stood its ground, a black-faced animal that held Ann's gaze as she passed, its jaw working on a hank of grass. 'Good afternoon, Mr Sheep,' she called, saluting the way her mum had taught her to greet magpies. The sheep blinked, and its tail flickered from side to side as it pushed a sequence of turds onto the ground behind it.

Ann found Jim further uphill, idly whacking a bush with a stick. The climb became a descent, and before long they stepped off the earth track onto the tarmac of the Withypool road. Ferns covered the high banks on either side, and branches of oak and beech joined to form a tunnel. Soon they were passing stone cottages and barns, the only signs of life the threads of smoke rising from chimneys.

They had booked a room at the Willow Tree, whose custard-yellow walls and blue windows reminded Ann of a witch's gingerbread house. She eased herself gratefully onto the bench of a trestle table that stood on a flagstone terrace above the road. The only other people drinking outdoors were a man and woman with a pair of velvet brown pointers lying at their feet. The dogs stayed down, but their eyes rebounded from Jim to Ann to their owners. The owners nodded hello, and continued their conversation in low voices.

'Drink?' Jim said.

'Oh god yes,' said Ann, smiling. 'Guinness. Pint please.' Jim went inside the pub. Ann took off her boots and stretched her legs. They had walked more than ten miles of hilly ground that day, and now she was sitting down she felt like she might never stand up. Her legs were packed with wet sand. The dogs regarded her, their sides swelling and shrinking in unison. Looking up from them, she found the man staring at her. The woman, her back to Ann, was hunting through her bag for something. The man took a sip from his pint, his eyes never leaving Ann's. She knew what that look wanted. He was rangy, strong-looking in brown Barbour and muddy jeans. His sharp jaw was mossed with a couple of days' growth of beard, his eyes were dark, unblinking. Then the woman produced a lighter from her bag, and the man turned towards her and pushed a pack of cigarettes across the table.

Jim returned with two black pints. The stout was cold and thick and Ann drank deeply, the beer's creamy head forming a moustache that spread from her nostrils to her cheeks. Jim laughed, then tipped his glass so far back that he coated his nose, and rivulets brown as river water streaked across his cheeks to his ears. Now Ann laughed. The dog owners looked on in silence. Screw yourselves, Ann thought, thinking she might as well enjoy herself even as it all collapsed. She raised her pint in another toast. They clashed glasses and gulped down the cold, black beer.

From the window of their low-ceilinged room at the top of the inn Ann saw the purple and brown heights of Exmoor rising in the distance, beyond ranks of beech, oak and birch. She was wearing a towel and kneeling on the worn cushions of a bench seat. The bedside lamps threw out a bronze light. From the bathroom came the sound of running water.

Jim leaned out of the bathroom door, eyebrows arched. 'I think we can both fit in that tub, you know.'

'Sounds good to me,' Ann said. 'You get in, I'll be there in a second.'

She heard a gasp of pleasure and pain as Jim eased himself into the hot water. Ann fetched her phone to take a picture of the twilight view. The grey sky and green trees – not a trace of autumn visible yet – blended in a vividness she knew a photograph wouldn't capture, but she tried anyway. She viewed the image: useless. Better just to look at it, she thought.

Jim called her name. He was lying back in the bath. She motioned for him to lean forward and she took off her towel, placed it on the tiled shelf at the end of the bath and sat on it. She held Jim's shoulders and moved him back so that he lay between her knees. His body was broad, and she needed to widely splay her legs to make room for him. She felt the surface of the hot water as a tightness around her shins. She leaned down, scooped up some water and poured it slowly over Jim's scalp. Slicked to his skull, his hair glistened like wet stone.

The day was ending and the bathroom, lit only by a skylight, was dim. In the near-dark Ann leaned Jim's body forward and washed his back. His pale skin shone faintly in the darkness. He murmured her name, his face close to the water. He reached an arm forward and turned the tap, adding hot water to the cooling bath. Ann's hands, coated in soap foam, worked their way from his neck down to his kidneys. She ran the sides of her thumbs up over the ridges of his spine. She noticed a chain of moles, flush with his skin, running along his shoulder blades. She put her hands in the water and cleared his back of soap. He started to lean back but she pushed him forward again. He rested his face on his knees. He said something she couldn't make out. She put her finger on the leftmost mole and walked her hand across them, left to right and right to left. 'You're marked,' she said. She waited for a reply, but all she heard was the deep, oblivious breath of a man asleep.

'Do you think we'd have made it across?' Ann asked at dinner in the pub dining room.

'Across what?' Jim said, around a mouthful of steak.

'The stepping stones.'

'Oh. Yeah. Sure. Why?'

'I don't know. You seemed... scared?'

'Scared?' Jim's cutlery clattered against his plate. A couple at the table beside them turned at the sound. 'Are you serious? Course I wasn't scared. A bit cautious, maybe, that's all.'

'My mistake.'

'Listen,' Jim said, straightening in his seat, 'wet gear is no joke—'

Ann started to smile. 'What's funny?' he said. She only shrugged, as if to say it wasn't important.

After dinner she suggested a walk, but Jim said he was tired and they had an early start in the morning. 'Bit too dark and scary out there for me, anyway,' he added, which she had to give him credit for. She thought about going out on her own, but found she was too tired, after all. Back in the room they undressed, put on robes that had been left out for them, and lay on the bed watching TV. Ann felt restless. She was bored by what they were watching, and rolled on her back to stare at the beams in the ceiling, listening to the film Jim was so absorbed in. It was about a series of bank robberies, each more elaborate and violent than the last. When it ended Jim said he was going to sleep. Ann asked if he minded her light being on. 'No,' he said, but instead of turning away put his arms around her and gathered her towards him. She opened her mouth to his kiss. One last time, she thought. Why not? His hand moved inside her robe. His thumb began circling the nipple. She drew him down on top of her. She closed her eyes and saw him striding away from her up the ridge, away from the river. He entered her and she felt a lump at her throat that she let out in a low moan. The river ran fast past the stepping stones, another world away. He pulled out of her, his quick breath hot against her cheek. She gripped him and squeezed, feeling the semen surge across her belly. He rolled off her and reached down with his hand and fumbled at her until she pushed his hand away. 'Sleep,' she said. He murmured something and again moved his hand towards her, but she pushed it back again. She reached up and switched off the light. She lay in the dark listening to the sound – so faint – of purling water. She started to touch herself and pushed herself back against the mattress. She was crossing the room, opening the door. The stairs creaked. The boot room was cold. She climbed away from the village, up past the rivulets' trickle and wash, past silent trees and sleeping sheep, and emerged at the top of the ridge above the river. Moonlight frosted the fields and scorched the water silver. Descending, the water's noise grew. The moon lay on the river in a serrated white line, stretching and gathering with the water's movement.

The stones were a chain of black squares in the liquid silver. Across the water rose the mass of the moor. On the far bank he stood, in his Barbour and jeans. She crossed the stones, flecks of icy water against her shins. He crossed, and they met in the river's flow. He pushed her down and was inside her. She straddled him and worked herself up and down the length of him. She pressed her palms against the cold, wet rock. As she came she leaned down into the fast-running brightness of the water, plunging her face into its icy grip.

———————

When Ann woke her irritation with Jim had swollen into anger. They ate breakfast in near silence, and exchanged few words as they walked. She had decided that when they reached that day's goal she would tell Jim she was going back to London. All she wanted was to be away from him.

The day was cloudy and cool: good for walking. They decided to avoid roads, so their route bypassed the village of Exford and took them towards a smaller crossing over the Exe. About half a mile before that, however, they came to a fast, narrow stream just ten feet across that wasn't marked on the map. The banks on both sides were very steep: the grey water, crested in places with curds of white foam, hissed past a good six feet below them. A split tree trunk had been laid between the banks, long ago judging by how embedded in the path it was.

Ann saw Jim hesitate, looking downstream and then up. 'I'm sure there's a long way round,' she said. 'Better safe than sorry, right?'

Jim turned and started to say something, then turned away. He walked onto the log bridge and was halfway across – Ann had just placed a foot on the splintered wood – when he lost his balance, crouched, yanked himself back upright for a moment, then flipped backwards and down into the water. He was carried under the bridge and Ann saw his head strike a group of jagged stones. He lay face down in the water. Carried swiftly, he was snatched round a bend and was gone, and it was that Ann never forgot: the terrible speed of it.

Never trust the good times

Chris Power on The Crossing

Chris Power is a gamekeeper turned poacher; his series, A Brief Survey of the Short Story, has run in The Guardian since 2007 – long before he published his own Edge Hill-shortlisted collection, Mothers, *in 2018 published by Faber and Faber.*

Here, Chris applies a forensic sensitivity to his own work, tracing the stages he went through, reflecting on what he kept and what he cut out – revealing how his broad understanding of the form allowed him to understand 'how much the story can bear.'

What was your starting point for this story? The characters? Or the idea of a crossing or threshold?

In this instance I definitely started with the sense of place. I recently talked to M John Harrison who said that writing should always come from place. It certainly works for him.

'The Crossing' very much started in its sense of place for a pretty prosaic reason – the inspiration for it came from a walking holiday I went on with my wife, along the border of Somerset and Devon. I was really enchanted by the landscape. We walked for a few days and I took lots of notes. The land we moved through was pretty much as it was laid out in the story, down to how the water was moving and all the physical details.

However, when I returned to the landscape in my writing, I started populating it with characters, which, for my wife's sake, I must say were very different to us. She always reminds me of that lovely walking holiday of ours that I completely ruined with my story, which has now largely supplanted the reality of our time together.

And where did these characters come from?

Maybe it was a question of opposites. My wife and I had a very harmonious time; we crossed this river just as it's described in the story. But there was something about that communal and bonding event that wormed away at me – stories thrive on conflict so I'm always playing with scenarios, searching for the stresses and strains that can take root there.

You didn't trust the good time you were having?

No, you can never trust the good times.

I think I was interested in the idea of these people being stuck. There was something about the way we were travelling – looking up a BnB in the morning and then striking out on a 12 mile walk to reach it – something about that was exciting. But I suppose the pessimistic writer side of me was thinking that there was something about the journey that could be a nightmare, as well as something about the journey itself that had an allegorical element to it. And I was drawn to the idea of compressing a relationship into the timespan of the journey itself.

When you first decided to write about Ann and Jim, what did you want to explore in their relationship?

The kernel of their relationship was their fractiousness. I wanted to explore the idea of this couple who were jarring against each other. But it took me a while to come to a decision about the nature of their relationship – how long they had been together, what they had shared and not shared – so that, together with other aspects of the story, it took me a lot of manoeuvring until I found the right range for them.

Your story touches very primal 'collective unconscious' archetypes such as the river, the crossing, light and dark, sex and death, spirit and redundancy. Was this an intentional decision of yours?

It was a much more allegorical story to begin with. In early drafts, the story definitely was very explicitly allegorical towards the end – when Jim falls asleep in the hotel and Ann dreams about going back to the stepping stones.

But I found this explicit allegorical style an uncomfortable fit – I wanted it to have that quality but when it was explicit, the story didn't work as well. It lived in that state for a while. I submitted it to a great editor, Brendan Barrington at the Dublin Review of Books and he identified this point of fracture within it.

So I spent a lot more time with it and rewrote it many times. I found that it really generated more of the kind of power or energy I wanted when I moved it towards realism: I found that with realistic writing the metaphorical elements were still there, and detectable, but without being at the forefront of the story.

This way it was possible to experience the story both as a concrete thing – a journey through a rural landscape – and a metaphor. They weren't fighting each other; in fact they were abetting one another. It taught me how to allow the metaphor in without it needing to become allegorical.

As you redrafted the story, how smooth and linear was your progression towards the finished version of the story?

'Linear' would be too graceful a description of it. A better description would be 'piecemeal', as there were sections I hung onto and sections I got rid of. The story began originally with

Never trust the good times

Ann wandering off because she hears a machine working away in the woods, which was something I really heard on our walk, an insane loud rattling noise from some machine I could not see. But a friend of mine, who's an amazing writer and a great note-giver, called attention to this opening and questioned this section.

With this story, as with several others in my book *Mothers*, I found that when I write from reality it often takes me a while to work out what is really relevant to the story and what I should let go of.

I think it's natural to want to keep certain things in early drafts simply because they're things that really happened, but as the story develops you have to really interrogate each one and be prepared to jettison them if they're getting in the way, or fail to manifest some kind of narrative purpose.

I don't really hold to the idea that not a single word can be wasted in a short story, but if a story is like a room you definitely want to carry out a dejunking process as you go.

'The Crossing' took a long time to get right (by which I mean right in terms of the balance of elements that I was trying to create): I would say that introduction was one false trail, but another was her dream of returning to the stepping stones, which was always the crux of the story, but in earlier drafts was more of a waking dream. In early versions, she actually gets up and goes out into the landscape, which made the physical and mental and spiritual more confusingly intermingled in the story. When I had pared this scene back, I found the rest of it took on a more defined shape and once I had that, after a few more drafts, I was able to arrive at what I wanted.

Echoes of the river occur throughout the story. How often and how explicitly did you want your theme to recur? Was this something you decreased or increased as you edited?

I think that thematic sense was there early on to a greater

degree than in my other stories in this collection. As I said earlier, this story started with a metaphorical idea of the journey. Typically when I write a story, the themes become apparent later on: then I edit towards or away from them – that is to say, amplify or somehow disguise them – as suits the story.

But in this story I think a lot of the details that echo throughout – the Guinness and the river water, for instance – were there from the off, and intended, and others were there but unintended. Then there were some I only saw openings for at a much later stage, once the story was more defined.

It was when I was editing that I was bringing the levels up or down, deciding what was too much and what was the right amount. By this I mean that sense of how much the story can bear, what will profit the story or what will make it overdetermined. Of course those parameters will be different for different people, but in this instance I really wanted to crystallise the driving linearity of the story. It's a journey starting in a specific place and ending in a specific place, so it has a directness at its heart. I didn't want to deviate from that line.

As a side note, you can write short stories that are so concentrated that they head only in one direction or you can write stories that digress and have the scope for things to fall off the page; in this case, because the story was so focused, it appealed to me to amplify those echoes and crosscurrents in the story.

How far was the story determined by your choice of Ann as the character through which we understand the events?

The narrative is filtered through Ann's consciousness because when I originally thought about the story, I had focused on Ann being stuck in this terrible situation with Jim, who's a terrible arse.

But now as I re-read it, I enjoy the fact that seeing it from her perspective carries some bias. Even though Jim is undoubtedly a bit of a dick, you could also write it from his aspect without altering any of the exchanges and think somewhat differently about the situation.

I suppose that's the power of the close third person narrator – you can develop sympathy with the character you are seeing the world through despite their flaws; I don't mean relatability or likeability, I mean just the fact of being close to them and seeing the world slightly through their eyes creates a connection to that character. Re-reading the story, I found the events less clear cut than I remembered, and I saw that Ann's perspective inflects the story as much as the overarching archetypes do.

After your initial idea, how did you set about moving this story in the direction you chose?

An important part of writing is just starting from any kind of impulse or aspect of the story, whatever gets you going. But then of course the story you think you're writing invariably, chimera-like, turns into something else in your hands. This makes for a destabilising period when you question your story, this new story you weren't expecting to be writing, until finally you become accommodated to it and you're able to realise what the story is, or the story tells you what it is. Then you can start writing towards that with a strong, or at least stronger, idea of where you have got to get to.

It's a process that could be broken into a period of blindness, then confusion, then hopefully some sort of direction.

You have got to get to the stage where you find the parameters are set, after which it's a question of writing within those parameters in the most stylish, engaging and thorough way possible.

Each stage is exciting and maddening in its own right. For example, in the final editing phase the difficulty is finding the things that belong outside the story and things that belong inside the story. However, it's also exciting because you're no longer looking at the terrifying snowy waste of the blank page, you're looking at these fields of possibility – like those that Ann sees when she looks across the stepping stones to those bright, empty fields, and seems to see a way out of her situation – and that's when you know you're working towards something rather than wandering at random. I find this a very motivating period of writing.

I read some advice you gave about the importance of a story's midpoint. Was this important for you in this story?

A writer I know said that she always looks at the absolute midpoint of the story, not so much as a failsafe test of a story, but more as a way of understanding its structure. The advice appealed to me; it feels right that something telling about the whole should be happening at the midpoint of the story, even if it's only something subtle. But I haven't actually gone back and checked to see if this is the case in my own work.

I felt it worked very well – your midpoint is the moment when Jim refused the second crossing, so... you did it!

So I did it! That's great. I'll tell my friend I passed her test.

The final paragraphs made for a shocking ending. Did you feel you had to throw short story readers 'off the scent' to surprise them?

No, I didn't, but I do find endings can be really hard. The greatest short story endings can leave a reader somewhat breathless in a huge variety of ways.

A reader can feel that great exhalation at the end either because they've been punched in the gut, or because some pressure has been exerted or lifted. Either are a sign that something is working in the story, but then again neither are absolutely necessary.

I love the way some of Chekhov's stories seem to dissolve in a mist, partly because as readers we've been held suspended for

Never trust the good times

the length of time we've been reading the story.

I've long railed, at tedious length and in various articles, against the trick ending. Take Maupassant's story 'The Necklace', for example: there the story is a mechanism, a very ingenious mechanism, that snaps shut at the end; that whole story is a trap, of sorts, and in the final lines the trap is sprung. But once you've experienced it, it's kind of exhausted, which feels like the opposite of art, or the art I like. I've always leaned more towards stories that conclude by opening out rather than snapping shut.

So, all that said, I was writing against type with 'The Crossing' because this is a story that snaps shut. Or appears to, at least. I resisted it for a little while – in earlier stages the story had a coda which went forward in time. In that ending Ann related the story to someone else, reflecting on this particular moment described at the story's close, and this brief relationship from earlier in her life and the impact it had on her.

But this coda didn't work at all, it just wasn't right. It sat there throughout various drafts as something I needed to try and improve. I must have written those last lines maybe fifty times, reordering them, using different methods, different amounts of detail.

Instead of using flashback, or going back and forth between the past and the present, I wanted to retain the main action lasting over a single span of time because I wanted the story to have an Aristotelian unity and happen in one place in one time frame. The story starts off accompanying them on the walk and, though Ann thinks back to when she first met Jim, aside from that there's no real flashback. Nearly all the story holds to this except in its last line, where we jump forward with the words: "it was that Ann never forgot: the terrible speed of it."

In the space of those last few words the story suddenly telescopes in time, but in such a way – and so quickly and briefly – that it almost doesn't register as a temporal shift.

I was pleased that I could arrive at an ending that worked

against my normal habits. I have written other stories that aren't nearly so final or so definitive; they tend to receive a variety of responses, from 'That ending was amazing,' to 'So why didn't you bother writing an ending?'

I've been very pleased to note that during the lifetime of this collection *Mothers*, lots of different people have cited different stories as being their particular favourite. But with 'The Crossing' the comment I hear most is: 'Holy shit! That ending!'

It feels that the sense of threat often increases and then ebbs. Was this 'lapping' rhythm of the tension intentional and why did you use it?

I really enjoy work that makes me feel tense when I'm reading it. For example, I love Roberto Bolaño's work and the way he can infuse any situation with tension – it could be someone walking down a familiar street, or through an empty house. Often no specific threat materialises, but he infuses every line with tension in a very subtle, undemonstrative way.

I love the way a story can drop into different registers, and can even feel like a ghost story even though nothing supernatural is going on. That certainly has influenced me: I'm always looking for situations that I can make tense. Or rather, it's better to say I find myself writing in a way that identifies or amplifies the tension in, say, walking through a field and describing the trees and the countryside. Outer reality is always coloured by what's going on in our heads, there's nothing controversial about that, so it seems to follow that the most everyday situation can be freighted with tension. In that way, place carries a story's emotional content just as much as the dialogue or physical interaction of the characters.

Relatedly, I find it really enjoyable when something has an eerie edge without it being explicitly supernatural. For example, in Mothers there's a story called 'The Haväng Dolmen.' It's a kind of ghost story, but although I really wanted to write a ghost story I found I couldn't go all the way, I needed it to be explicable as a man going through a mental crisis – I realised in the course of writing it that I couldn't just depart realism, that I'm quite bound to it. 'The Crossing' was actually one of the stories that taught me that, because when I tried to write it in a more Lawrentian style, or like T.F. Powys – more explicitly metaphorical – I found there was something off with it. I didn't have the ability to make it work in relation to the other stories in the collection which are all realistic – even the ghost story.

Did you draw inspiration from other writers to write this story? For example when you were so specific about the 'seventeen' stepping stones, I was reminded of Ford Madox Ford's comment about DH Lawrence's precision in the opening of 'The Odour of Chrysanthemums': "this man knows what he wants. He sees the scene of his story exactly."

Everything you hoover up in your reading gets sucked and churned up inside you. There are definitely things that have influenced me and things I've borrowed-slash-stolen from writers. I read something once that said in one painting by Constable he copied a tree from a painting by some Renaissance artist. I like that idea of artistic influence being just like sampling in music; I like the idea that you can go to a gallery and say: 'I like that, I'll have that tree or that hand.'

Writing is similar, in the sense that writers have a bedrock of influences they have built up over time. You couldn't necessarily identify all of them, though – I mean I couldn't begin to identify all of my own – because they're such a mixture of different things.

Most writers read very widely and all that mashes together in their writing. Sometimes, in spite of what I just said, you can notice these influences very clearly in yourself. For example, you may notice you're transitioning between scenes the way another writer does, or you're copying the way they describe a path in the forest. In these cases, the influence lodges in your mind and you can choose to stop yourself from copying the technique.

But other times your influences will inflect your writing in a way that you're just not conscious of. Sometimes a reader might say to you that this story really reminds them of so and so, and when you go and read so and so you think: *This is great; I'm glad I'm being compared to this person!*

To answer your question about the stepping stones in 'The Crossing', the details are so specific because I was recording them all in a notebook as I went. But now the details of the story have supplanted my real memories and I couldn't hand on heart say there really were seventeen stones. But I wouldn't be surprised if there were.

When I was drafting the story I had a number of browser tabs open on the flora and fauna of the West Country. I'm not great on the natural world but I wanted to name things, I wanted Ann to be engaged in the landscape in that way. I didn't want to go too far and have her be hyper-aware, because that kind of fetishised level of detail can get in the way – the reader doesn't necessarily need to know if something's saxifrage or whatever – but I did want there to be some sort of life and specific sense of England to the landscape they're walking in. So when talking about influences, maybe the biggest overt influences in this case were the RHS and Woodland Trust websites.

Mrs Fox

by Sarah Hall

That he loves his wife is unquestionable. All day at work he looks forward to seeing her. On the train home, he reads, glancing up at the stations of commuter towns, land-steal under construction, slabs of mineral-looking earth, and pluming clouds. He imagines her robe falling as she steps across the bedroom. Usually he arrives first, while she drives back from her office. He pours a drink and reclines on the sofa. When the front door opens he rouses. He tries to wait, for her to come and find him, and tell him about her day, but he hasn't the patience. She is in the kitchen, taking her coat off, unfastening her shoes. Her form, her essence, a scent of corrupted rose.

Hello, darling, she says.

The shape of her eyes, almost Persian, though she is English. Her waist and hips in the blue skirt; he watches her move – to the sink, to the table, to the chair where she sits, slowly, with a woman's grace. Under the hollow of her throat, below the collar of her blouse, is a dribble of fine gold, a chain, on which hangs her wedding ring.

Hello, you.

He bends to kiss her, his hands in his pockets. Such simple pleasure; she is his to kiss. He, or she, cooks; this is the modern world, both of them are capable, both busy. They eat dinner, sometimes they drink wine. They talk or listen to music; nothing in particular. There are no children yet.

Later, they move upstairs and prepare for bed. He washes his face, urinates. He likes to leave the day on his body. He wears nothing to sleep in; neither does his wife, but she has showered, her hair is damp, darkened to wheat. Her skin is incredibly soft; there is no corrugation on her rump. Her pubic hair is harsh when it dries; it crackles against his palm, contrasts strangely with what's inside. A mystery he wants to solve every night. There are positions they favour, that feel and make them appear unusual to each other. The trick is to remain slightly detached. The trick is to be able to bite, to speak in a voice not your own. Afterwards, she goes to the bathroom, attends to herself, and comes back to bed. His sleep is blissful, dreamless.

Of course, this is not the truth. No man is entirely contented. He has stray erotic thoughts, and irritations. She is slow to pay bills. She is messy in the bathroom; he picks up bundles of wet towels every day. Occasionally, he uses pornography, if he is away for work. He fantasises about other women, some of whom look like old girlfriends, some like his wife. If a woman at work or on the train arouses him, he wonders about the alternative, a replacement. But in the wake of these moments, he suffers vertiginous fear, imagines losing her, and he understands what she means. It is its absence which defines the importance of a thing.

And what of this wife? She is in part unknowable, as all clever women are. The marrow is adaptable, which is not to say she is guileful, just that she will survive. Only once has she been unfaithful. She is desirable, but to elicit adoration there must be more than sexual qualities. Something in her childhood has made her withheld. She makes no romantic claims, does not require reassurance, and he adores her because of the lack. The one who loves less is always loved more. After she has cleaned herself and joined him in bed, she dreams subterranean dreams, of forests, dark corridors and burrows, roots and earth. In her purse, alongside the makeup and money, is a small purple ball. A useless item, but she keeps it – who can say why? She is called Sophia.

Their house is modern, in a town in the corona of the city. Its colours are arable: brassica, taupe, flax. True angles, long surfaces, invisible, soft-closing drawers. The mortgage is large. They have invested in bricks, in the concept of home. A cleaner comes on Thursdays. There are similar houses nearby, newly built along the edgelands, in the lesser countryside – what was once heath.

One morning he wakes to find his wife vomiting into the toilet. She is kneeling, retching, but nothing is coming up. She is holding the bowl. As she leans forward the notches in her spine rise against the flesh of her back. Her protruding bones, the wide-open mouth, a clicking sound in her gullet: the scene is disconcerting, his wife is almost never ill. He touches her shoulder.

Are you all right? Can I do anything?

She turns. Her eyes are bright, the brightness of fever. There is a coppery gleam under her skin. She shakes her head. Whatever is rising in her has passed. She closes the lid, flushes, and stands. She leans over the sink and drinks from the tap, not sips, but long sucks of water. She dries her mouth on a towel.

I'm fine.

She lays a hand, briefly, on his chest, then moves past him into the bedroom. She begins to dress, zips up her skirt, fits her heels into the backs of her shoes.

I won't have breakfast. I'll get something later. See you tonight.

She kisses him goodbye. Her breath is slightly sour. He hears the front door slam and the car engine start. His wife has a strong constitution. She does not often take to her bed. In the year they met she had some kind of mass removed, through an opened abdomen; she got up and walked the hospital corridors the same day. He goes into the kitchen and cooks an egg. Then he too leaves for work. Later, he will wonder, and through the day he worries. But that evening, when they return to the house, will herald only good things. She seems well again, radiant even, having signed a new contract at work for the sale of a block of satellite offices. The greenish hue to her skin is gone. Her hair is undone and all about her shoulders. She pulls him forward by his tie.

Thank you for being so sweet this morning. They kiss. He feels relief, but over what he's not sure. He untucks her blouse, slips his fingers under the waistband of her skirt. She indicates her willingness. They move upstairs and reduce each other to nakedness. He bends before her. A wide badge of hair, undepilated, spreads at the top of her thighs. The taste reminds him of a river. They take longer than usual. He is strung between immense climactic pleasure and delay. She does not come, but she is ardent; finally he cannot hold back. They eat late – cereal in bed – spilling milk from the edges of the bowls, like children. They laugh at the small domestic adventure; it's as if they have just met.

Tomorrow is the weekend, when time becomes luxurious. But his wife does not sleep late, as she usually would. When he wakes she is already up, in the bathroom. There is the sound of running water, and under its flow another sound, the low cry of someone expressing injury, a burn, or a cut, a cry like a bird, but wider of throat. Once, twice, he hears it. Is she sick again? He knocks on the door.

Sophia?

She doesn't answer. She is a private woman; this is her business. Perhaps she is fighting a flu. He goes to the kitchen to make coffee. Soon she joins him. She has bathed and dressed but does not look well. Her face is pinched, dark around the eye sockets, markedly so, as if an overnight gauntening has taken place. Oh, poor you, he says. What would you like to do today? We could stay here and take it easy, if you don't feel well.

Walk, she says. I'd like some air.

He makes toast for her but she takes only a bite or two. He notices that the last chewed mouthful has been put back on her plate, a damp little brown pile. She keeps looking towards the window.

Would you like to go for a walk now? he asks. She nods and stands. At the back door she pulls on leather boots, a coat, a yellow scarf, and moves restlessly while he finds his jacket. They walk through the cul de sac, ringed by calluna houses, past the children's play area at the end of the road, the concrete pit with conical mounds where children skate. It is still early; no one is around. Intimations of frost under north-facing gables. Behind the morning mist, a faint October sun has begun its industry. They walk through a gateway onto scrubland, then into diminutive trees, young ash, recently planted around the skirt of the older woods. Two miles away, on the other side of the heath, towards the city, bulldozers are levelling the earth, extending the road system.

Sophia walks quickly on the dirt path, perhaps trying to walk away the virus, the malaise, whatever it is that's upsetting her system. The path rises and falls, chicanes permissively. There are ferns and grasses, twigs angling up, leaf-spoils, the brittle memory of wild garlic and summer flowers. Towards the centre, a few older trees have survived; their branches heavy, their bark flaking, trunks starred with orange lichen. Birds dip and dart between bushes. The light breaks through; a gilded light, terrestrial but somehow holy.

She moves ahead. They do not speak, but it is not uncompanionable. He allows himself, for a few moments, to be troubled by irrational thoughts – she has a rapid, senseless cancer and will waste, there will be unconscionable pain, he will hold a fatal vigil beside her bed. Outliving her will be dire. Her memory will be like a wound in him. But, as he watches her stride in front, he can see that she is fit and healthy. Her body swings, full of energy. What is it then? An unhappiness? A confliction? He dares not ask.

The woods begin to thicken: oak and beech. A jay flaps across the thicket, lands on the ground nearby; he admires the primary blue elbow before it flutters off. Sophia turns her head sharply in the direction of its flight. She picks up her pace and begins to walk strangely on the tips of her toes, her knees bent, her heels lifted. Then she leans forward and in a keen, awkward position begins to run. She runs hard. Her feet toss up fragments of turf and flares of leaves. Her hair gleams – the chromic sun renders it livid. She runs, at full tilt, as if pursued.

Hey, he calls. Hey! Stop! Where are you going? Fifty yards away, she slows and stops. She crouches on the path as he hurries after her, her body twitching in an effort to remain still. He catches up.

What was all that about? Darling?

She turns her head and smiles. Something is wrong with her face. The bones have been re-carved. Her lips are thin and her nose is a dark blade. Teeth small and yellow. The lashes of her hazel eyes have thickened and her brows are drawn together, an expression he has never seen, a look that is almost craven. A trick of kiltering light on this English autumn morning. The deep cast of shadows from the canopy. He blinks. She turns to face the forest again. She is leaning forward, putting her hands down, lifting her bottom. She has stepped out of her laced boots and is walking away. Now she is running again, on all fours, lower to earth, sleeker, fleeter. She is running and becoming smaller, running and becoming smaller, running in the light of the reddening sun, the red of her hair and her coat falling, the red of her fur and her body loosening. Running. Holding behind her a sudden, brazen object, white tipped. Her yellow scarf trails in the briar. All vestiges shed.

She stops, within calling distance, were he not struck dumb. She looks over her shoulder. Topaz eyes glinting. Scorched face. Vixen.

October light, no less duplicitous than any season's. Bird calls. Plants shrivelling. The moon, palely bent on the horizon, is setting. Everything, swift or slow, continues. He looks at the fox on the path in front of him. Any moment, his wife will walk between the bushes. She will crawl out of the wen of woven ferns. The undergrowth, which must surely have taken her, will yield her. How amazing, she'll whisper, pointing up the track.

These are his thoughts, standing in the morning sun, staring, and wrestling belief. Insects pass from stalk to stalk. The breeze through the trees is sibilant.

On the path, looking back at him, is a brilliant creature, which does not move, does not flinch or sidle off. No. She turns fully and hoists the tail around beside her like a flaming sceptre. Slim limbs and slender nose. A badge of white from jaw to breast. Her head thrust low and forward, as if she is looking along the earth into the future. His mind's a shock of useless thought, denying, hectoring, until one lone voice proceeds through the chaos. You saw, you saw, you saw. He says half words, nothing sensible. And now she trots towards him down the path, as a dog would, returning to its master.

Nerve and instinct. Her thousand feral programmes. Should she not flee into the borders, kicking away the manmade world? She comes to him, her coy, sporting body held on elegant black-socked legs. A moment ago: Sophia. He stands still. His mind stops exchanging. At his feet, she sits, her tail rearing. Exceptional, winged ears. Eyes like the spectrum of her blended fur. He kneels, and with absolute tenderness, touches the ruff of her neck, which would be soft, were it not for the light tallowing of hairs.

What can be decided in a few moments that will not be questioned for a lifetime? He collects her coat from the nearby bushes. He moves to place it, gently, around her – she does not resist – and, his arms reaching cautiously under, he lifts her. The moderate weight of a mid-sized mammal. The scent of musk, gland, and faintly, faintly, her perfume – a dirty rose.

And still, in the woods and on the apron of grass land, no one is hiking, though soon there will be dogs tugging against leads, old couples, children gadding about. Down the path he walks, holding his fox. Her brightness escapes the coat at both ends; it is like trying to wrap fire. Her warmth against his chest is astonishing – for a wife who always felt the cold, in her hands and feet. She is calm; she does not struggle, and he bears her like a sacrifice, a forest Pietà.

Half a mile in secret view. Past the sapling ash trees, through the heath gate, past the concrete pit where one sole girl is turning tricks on her board, practising before the boys come, her gaze held down over the front wheels. There are the houses – new builds, each spanking, chimneyless, their garages closed – and he must walk the gauntlet of suburbia, his heart founding a terrible rhythm at the thought of doors opening, blinds being lifted, exposure. Somewhere nearby a car door slams. She shifts in his arms and his grip tightens. Around the bend; he ignores the distracted neighbour who is moving a bin. Up the pathway to number 34. She is heavier now, deadening his muscles. He moves her to the crux of his left arm, reaches into his trouser pocket for the keys, fumbles, drops them, bends down. She, thinking he is releasing her perhaps, begins to wriggle and scramble towards the ground, but he keeps her held in his aching arm, he lifts the keys from the flagstones, opens the door and enters. He closes the door behind and all the world is shut out. Suddenly his rescuer's strength goes. His arms give. Sensing it, she jumps, her back claws raking his forearm. She lands sheerly on the carpet. She holds still a second or two, shakes, then goes into the kitchen, directly, no investigation of location, and jumps onto a chair next to the table. As if only now, after her walk and purging of the disease of being human, she is ready for breakfast.

These first hours with his new wife pass, not in wonderment, nor in confusion or fugue, but in a kind of acute discerning. She positions herself in the house, wherever she fancies, as she might otherwise have. He follows, making sure she has not vanished, making sure he is conscious. The spectacular evidence remains. He is able to approach.

He is able to touch the back of her head, under the slim, almost bearded jaw, even the pads of her paws, which are so sensitive her flesh quivers. Like a curious lover he studies her form. The remarkable pelt, forged as if in a crucible of ruddy, igneous landscapes. The claws that have left long angry scratches on his arm: crescent-shaped, blond and black. The triangular, white-lined ears, with tall, dark guard hairs. The bend in her hind legs; the full, shapely thighs, similar, in a way, to a woman squatting. He studies sections, details. Her eyes, up close, are the colour of the Edwardian citrine brooch he bought her for her birthday.

He speaks quietly, says things she might want to hear, consolations. I am sorry. It will be all right. The day is lost. For much of it she sleeps. She sleeps curled on the floor. Her ribs palpitate. As dusk arrives he tries to eat, but can't. He picks her up and carries her to the bed. She repositions and closes her eyes again. Gently, he lies down next to her. He puts a hand to her side, where she is reddest. The texture of her belly is smooth and delicate, like scar tissue; small nubbed teats under the fur. Her smell is gamey; smoky, sexual.

Sophia, he whispers, don't worry, though she is not, as far as he can tell, distressed.

He closes his eyes. Sleep, the cure for all catastrophes, will bring relief, perhaps even reverse. When he wakes there is the faint lunar bloom of streetlight in the bedroom and she is gone. He starts up. He moves through the house, desperately, like a man searching for a bomb. No dream could ever be so convincing. He rushes downstairs, and at the bottom treads in something slightly crusted and yielding. Quickly, he searches on. He calls out her name, feeling ever more its falseness.

She is standing on the kitchen table, an unmistakable silhouette, cut from the wild. She is looking out of the French windows at the garden, the nocturnal world. She is seeing what alien sights? The fresnel lenses of owl's eyes, luminous grassy trails, or bats blurting across the lawn? The grisly aroma of what he has trodden in rises to his nose. He wipes his foot on the carpet. He sits at the table and puts his head in his hands. She watches the garden.

Sunday. Monday. He fields phone calls from his and her places of work. He manages to lie convincingly, asks for personal leave. There is no milk. He drinks black tea. He eats cold soup, a stump of staling bread. He puts down bowls of water on the kitchen floor, but either she does not like the purity or the chlorine. He sits for hours, thinking, silent – every time he speaks he feels the stupidity of words. What has happened? Why? He is not able to unlock anything reasonable in his mind. She is in the house, a bright mass, a beautiful arch being, but he feels increasingly alone. He does not let her out, cruel as it seems, though she pays particular attention to the doors and vents where small draughts of outside air can be felt and smelled – he watches her sniffing the seal, gently clawing the frame. If this does not pass, he thinks, he will take himself to the doctor, or her to the veterinary – one of them will discover the truth, the contraspective madness. But then, how can he?

The sound of a key in the front-door lock startles him. He has been lying naked on the bedroom floor while she patrols. It is Esmé, the cleaner. It is Thursday. Nine a.m. He pulls on a robe, dashes down the stairs, and catches her just as she is coming into the hallway, dropping her bag on the floor, the door gaping open behind her.

No, he shouts. No! Go away. You have to go. He puts a hand on her shoulder and begins to manoeuvre her backwards, towards the door. She gasps in shock at such treatment. Her employer is never home when she cleans – all she knows of him is the money he leaves on the table, the addressed letters she moves from doormat to counter, and it's his wife who speaks to her on the phone. She barely recognises him, and for a moment mistakes him for an intruder.

What? What? Take your hands off. I, I'll – She is alarmed, he can see, at the blockade, at being handled by a dishevelled, undressed man.

He gathers his wits, releases her arm.

Don't clean this week, Esmé. We have a terrible bug. It's very contagious. I don't want to risk you getting it.

He is pale, a little crazed, but does not look ill. Sophia has it? Yes. She does.

Does she need anything? I can go to the pharmacy. I'm taking care of her. Thank you. Please –

He gestures for her to leave. Routed, Esmé picks up her bag and steps away. He closes the door behind her, moves to the hall window and watches. She glances up at the bedroom, frowns, walks to her little blue car, gets in, and drives away. When he turns round the fox is standing at the top of the stairs.

Later that day, tense with anxiety, he leaves the house and goes to the library. He researches the world of madness. *Folie à deux.* Imposter delusion. Cotard. Capgras. Madame Zero. Mineness and the self's relations. But is it she or he who is lost? Then: Transmogrification. Fables. If he can avail himself of understanding, reason, definition... He returns home with medical texts and a slender yellow volume from the twenties. There is little correlation to myth. He is no thwarted lover. Most upsetting is the repetition of one aspect: an act of will.

So it continues. He enters a room and at first does not notice that she is up on top of the cabinet, on the windowsill, in the sliding food rack, which he has left open. Her poise so still she is entirely missable, the way all wild things are, until the rustic outline comes into focus. The surprise of seeing her, every time, in proximity; a thing from another realm that he has brought home. She sleeps. She sleeps neatly in a circle, tail tucked under her chin. Not on the bed, where he keeps trying to put her, but on a chair seat, in the corner of the utility room. The house is warm but she makes the most of extra heat wherever she can find it – the seat he has just vacated, or under the boiler. He cleans away the black, twisted scat that he finds, almost odourless now, tries not to be disgusted. If we were old, he tells himself, if I were her carer. He leaves plates of food on the floor, milk-soaked bread, cooked chicken, inoffensive dishes, which she investigates, tries, but does not finish. Instead she looks up at him, her brows steepling, haughty, unsatisfied. Part of his brain will not translate what she wants: that she must have it raw. Her eyes flicker after birds in the garden. Even trapped behind glass, she calculates. The metrics of the hunt.

Hating the humiliation, he brings home a can of dogfood, tips the jellied lump out onto a china dinner plate. She rejects it. He finds her licking her lips and trotting out of the kitchen. On the expensive slate floor is a dark patch of saliva – she has eaten something, a spider perhaps.

He cannot speak to her anymore. She doesn't understand and his voice sounds ridiculous to his own ears, a cacophony. She will not tolerate being in the same room for long. She roams, sniffs at the back door. She wants what's outside, she is becoming restive, growling, but he knows he cannot let her go. What would become of her, and, with her, his hope? He inches around the front door when he leaves and locks it behind, is careful when re-entering the house. He phones and tells the cleaning woman her services are no longer needed.

And he knows; in this terrible arrangement, it is he who is not adjusting; he who is failing their relationship. So he decides. He buys uncooked meat from the butcher, offal, and in a moment of bravado, throws it onto the floor in front of her. She nips at a purple lobe, then walks away. Surely she is hungry! You are a fool, he tells himself. The next day he goes to a specialty shop and brings home a live bird. A pigeon. Its wings are clipped. He sets it on the floor, where it hops and tries to lift. Within moments she is beside it, crouching, lit with energy. He watches as she recoils and then pounces high, higher than she need, in excitement or prowess, and comes down hard on the helpless flurrying thing. She bites its iridescent neck. She twists its head. She is like machinery; the snapping and clicking of her teeth. The lavender breast is opened; there are riches inside. He turns and leaves, feeling sickened. He is angry and ashamed. That she could ever, even before this, be his pet. It cannot go on – the proof is everywhere. Musk on the doorframes. Stains on the carpet. Downy feathers. And his unnatural longing, which can never be resolved, nor intimacy converted, even as his mind nudges against the possibility. Whatever godly or conjugal test this is, he has certainly failed. He decides. He opens the utility door and leaves it standing wide. He sits outside with his back against the cold house wall. In the garden is a muddy, mushroomy smell – tawny November. Under the trees, husks and hard fruits are furling and rotting. He waits. The pressure and temperature of the house changes, scents enter, great free gusts of coppice and bonfire and heath, and beyond, the city's miasma. It doesn't take long. Her head and shoulders come through the doorway. She pauses, one front paw lifted and pointing, her jaws parted, the folded tongue lifting up. He stares straight ahead. He tells himself it is not a choice. He does not want her to leave and yet he can no longer stand the lunacy, the impasse, his daily torment. Sophia has gone, he tells himself.

She bolts, a long streak of russet down the lawn, between the plum trees, and up over the fence, the white tip flashing like an afterthought.

He feels nothing. Not relief. Not sorrow. That night he leaves the back door standing open, love's caveat. In the morning there are slugs and silvery trails on the kitchen floor, sodden leaves blown in, and the bin has been knocked over. The following night he shuts the door, though does not lock it. His dreams are anguished, involving machinery and dogs, his own brutality, and blood.

Winter. A little snow, which gives England an older, calmer appearance. She has not come back. He worries about the cold, what might become of her, out there. There are distant nocturnal screams, like a woman being forced – are they hers? He checks the garden for signs, prints in the crisp skin of ice, her waste. The line he tells is one of simple separation. The neighbours do not ask further questions. A letter arrives from her place of work accepting termination of employment. All the while the enormity of what has happened haunts him. The knowledge might send him insane, he thinks. One day he will take off his clothes and lie in the street and beat his head with his fists and laugh as if choking. He will admit to killing her, beg for jail, though her body will never be found.

He returns to work. He is polite and, to new workers in the office, sullen-seeming. Those who know him, those who met his wife, understand some vital spark has been extinguished. He cannot quite reclaim himself. He feels victimhood strongly. Something has been taken from him. Taken, and in the absurdest possible way. He pities himself, abhors his passivity – could he not have done more? After a while it dawns on him that she doesn't want to come back, that perhaps she did not want what she had. An act of will. Her clothes hang in the wardrobe, until, one morning – the mornings are always easier and more decisive – he gathers them up, folds them carefully and places them in bags. He goes through the contents of her purse. They offer nothing enlightening, not even her lipstick, a red hue women can rarely wear, or the small purple ball, too gnomic to interpret. But these intimate items he cannot throw away. He places them in a bottom drawer.

Enough, he thinks.

He tries to forget. He tries to masturbate. He thinks of others, of partial, depersonalised images, obscenities; he concentrates, but release will not come. Instead, he weeps.

A week later, close to Christmas, he begins to walk on the heath again. That moulted protean place, which he has for months avoided. He walks at first light, when the paths are deserted, and the low red sun glimmers between bare twigs. He is not looking. He is not looking and yet he feels keenly aware of this old, colloquial tract of land, with its debris of nature, hemmed in by roads and houses, lathed away by bulldozers. It is fecund. It is rife with a minority of life-forms. Black birds in the stark arboretum, larval-looking and half-staged in the uppermost branches. The dead grass rustling. A flash of wing or leg. Sometimes he sits for a while, his collar turned up, his gloveless hands on the fallen trunk, whose sap is hard and radiant. His breath clouds the air. He is here, now. He would give himself, except there is no contract being offered.

He might find comfort in the sinew of winter, when nothing exists but that which is already exposed, and so he does, slowly, and as the earth tilts back towards the sun, his mind begins to ease a little. To be comfortable inside one's sadness is not valueless. This too will pass. All things tend towards transience, mutability. It is in such mindful moments, when everything is both held and released, that revelation comes.

So she appears on the path in front of him, in the budding early spring. He has been staring down at his feet as they progress, at the shivering stems and petals. All around him, the spermy smell of blossom. Yes, the world is saying, I begin. He looks up. The vixen is on a grass mound, twenty feet ahead. She is like a comet in the surroundings, her tail, her flame. She has her head lowered, as if in humility, as if in apology for her splendour, the black backs of her ears visible. Oh, her golden greening eyes. Her certainty of colour.

How easily she can fell him; and he will always fall.

She faces him. He waits to hear his name, just his name, that he could be made un-mad by it. She steps into the low scrub of the forest floor, takes a few high and tidy steps, and he thinks at first the wilderness has finally untamed her, she is afraid, about to run. But she turns, and pauses. Another step. A backward glance. What, then, is she piloting? Is he to follow?

The old, leftover stretch of heath, preserved by a tenuous council ruling, by councillors who dine in expensive restaurants with developers, has a crock of boulders and hardwoods at its centre. Moss. Thrift. Columbine. Tides of lesser vasculars. She picks her way in, a route invisible to his eye, but precisely marked, it seems. Rock to stump, she crosses and criss-crosses. She knows he is following; his footfalls are mortifying, though he tries to tread respectfully through this palace of delicate filaments. He keeps his distance. He must convey at all costs that he has no intention to touch her, take her, or otherwise destroy the accord. The roots of old trees rear out of the ground, pulling strings of soil up with them. These are earnest natives; they have survived blight and lightning and urban expansion. They bear the weight of mythical, hollow thrones. Lungs of fungi hang from their branches.

Beneath one trunk there is an opening, a gash between stones and earth. Her den. She makes a circuit of the nearby copse, then sits beside the entrance, laying her flaring tail alongside her. Her belly is pinkish and swollen. She is thinner than he remembered, her legs long and narrow-footed, like a deer's. She cocks her head, as if giving him licence to speak. But no, he must not think this way. Nothing of the past is left, except the shadow on his mind. From her slender jaw she produces a low sound, like a chirp, a strangled bark. She repeats it. He does not know what it means. In their house she was never vocal, except with displeasure. Then, from the dark gape, a sorrel cub emerges, its paws tentative on the den-run, its eyes opaque, bluish, until only recently blind, a charcoal vulpine face. Another follows, nudging the first. And another. There are four. They stumble towards their mother. They fit to her abdomen, scrambling for position, stepping on and over each other. As she feeds them her eyes blink closed, sensually, then she stares at him.

Privy to this, no man could be ready. Not at home, skulling the delivery within the bloody sheets, nor in the theatre gown, standing behind a screen as the surgeon extracts the child. The lovely sting in him! They are, they must be, his. He crouches slowly. She is thirled to the task, but not impatient. Before they are done she nudges the cubs away. They nose against each other. They rock, vulnerably, on their paws, licking the beads of milk from each other. A great inspirational feeling lets loose in him. He has sweeping masculine thoughts. He understands his duty. He swears silent oaths to himself and to her: that he will guard this secret protectorate. That he will forgo all else. He will, if it comes to it, lie down in front of any digger before it levels this shrine.

The cubs remain above ground a moment longer. They play in silence, programmed to safe mutism, while she watches. They have her full attention. Their coats are dirty, sandy camouflage, but nothing will be left to chance. She curtails their crèche. One by one, she lifts them by their scruffs towards the hole, sends them back inside, and then, without hesitating, disappears after.

As he leaves he memorises the way. The den is not as far from the path as he thought, dogs off their leads will detect their secretions, but it is secluded, lost behind a sward of bracken. She knows. His head is full of gold as he walks home. He allows himself the temporary glow of pride, and then relinquishes it. He has no role, except as guest. The truth is their survival is beyond his control.

He does not return every day, but once a week makes an early foray into the woods. He approaches respectfully, remains at a distance; a watcher, estranged. He never catches them out but must wait for an appearance. They materialise from the ground, from the undergrowth, an oak stump. If they know him they show no indication. Past a look or two – their eyes eerie and hazelish – they pay him no heed. Their mother has sanctioned his presence, that is all. The exclusion is gently painful, but it is enough to see them, to watch them grow.

And how rapidly they grow. The dark of their faces shrinks to two smuts either side of their noses. The orange fur begins to smoulder. Their ears become disproportionate. They are quick, ridiculously clumsy, unable to control their energy. He laughs, for the first time in months. Then their play turns savage, tumbling and biting. They learn to focus, peering at small moving quarry; they stalk, chew beetles, snap at airborne insects, while their mother lies in the grass, exhausted by them. She brings fresh carcasses, which they tug at, shaking their heads, twisting off strips of carrion. And still she feeds them her milk, though they are two thirds her size and he can see the discomfort of her being emptied, of manufacturing and lending nutrients. Sometimes she looks at him, as if waiting for his decision.

He is a man with two lives. He works, he holds conversations with office staff, shops at the supermarket. He turns down dates, but seems contented, and his colleagues wonder if he has, without declaration, moved on. Esmé is re-employed, though she is sad Sophia Garnett has left her husband and suspects injustice against her to be the cause – whatever that may be. But she finds no trace of any other woman in the house, no lace underwear, no lost earring or hairs gathered in the sink. The thoughts of murder pass.

He watches men lifting their children out of car seats and up from toppled bicycles. He watches them push swings. If anyone were to ask, he would say, I am not without happiness. He walks the heath. He monitors the landscape. He worries about the cubs, the multitude of dangers, even as they grow larger and stronger, and he can see all that they will be. They ambush their mother, who at times seems sallow, having sacrificed her quota of prey, having no mate to help her. They show interest in the rubbish of the woods, bringing back wrappers and foil, even the arm of a plastic doll. There will be dispersal, he knows, but not yet. For now, they are hers, and perhaps his, though peripherally.

One day an idea strikes him. He goes to the den site. They are not there, but he doesn't linger. He takes from his pocket the little purple ball Sophia used to keep in her purse. He places it by the entrance. The next time he comes it has vanished. He looks around until he finds it, lying under a thornbush nearby. He picks it up. There are teeth marks in the surface, scratches, signs of play. What will become of them he does not know. The woods are temporary and the city is rapacious. He has given up looking for meaning. Why, is a useless question, an unknowable object. Who, will never be known. But to suspend thought is impossible. The mind is made perfectly of possibilities. One day, Sophia might walk through the garden, naked, her hair long and tangled, her body gloried by use. She will open the back door, which is never locked, and enter the kitchen and sit at the table. I dreamt of the forest again, she will say.

It is a forgivable romance, high conceit – he knows. At night he lies in bed, not at its centre, but closer to the midway point. He thinks of Sophia, the woman he loved. He no more expects her to return than he conceived of her departure. But he imagines her stepping across the room, bare, and damp from the shower. And then he thinks of the fox, in her blaze, in her magnificence. It is she who quarters his mind, she whose absence strikes fear into his heart. Her loss would be unendurable. To watch her run into the edgelands, breasting the ferns and scorching the fields, to see her disappear into the void – no – how could life mean anything without his unbelonging wife?

I didn't realise what I'd done

Sarah Hall on Mrs Fox

'Mrs Fox' won the 2013 National Short Story Award, its judges 'seduced by its dexterity and poetic use of language'. It is probably this lyricism that makes asking questions about it feel a little like dissecting a unicorn.

Fittingly for a story as magical as this, Sarah wrote this undistracted by the technical aspects of craft. Instead, knowing only a few plot points, she created it from her instinctive feel for the story.

You open the story with a description of the couple's return home from work. Why did you feel this was the place you wanted to begin?

The word 'feel' is the important one here. Writing is often a feeling about what the shape should be, rather than it being a mechanical approach. I'm quite an automatic writer so I can get a sense of what I'm doing and *feel* that it's right.

Because this is a domestic story – though also about the wildness that is offset by the domestic – this felt like a very good way to enter what appears to be a pretty good relationship.

But it also opens with a discrepancy that the husband feels more for the wife, which is always an interesting place to start in relationships – this slight imbalance which, because it's a short story, is going to set something up later.

The first sentence in the story is key; 'that he loves his wife is unquestionable' – immediately we know this will be questioned. It also raises another question, which is: do you agree with the premise of that question? It is like opening a box of tricks; you enter this realm to seek an answer to the question but find, in fact, the question is challenged by the end because the whole dynamic has shifted to another realm.

But just having them arrive back from work and seeing their interaction was quite a nice way of setting up the characters, showing us the withholding she does and yet also their sexual chemistry. I wanted to give the sense that this is going to be a wild story but, in order for it to get wilder, it first needs to be domestic and show the ordinary interactions between a couple.

The voice seems to be both terse as well as primal and intoning. How did you come to this voice? Were you influenced by folklore?

When the voice arrives, it hopefully has a spectrum. Grown-ups are fairly complicated things anyway so, whatever voice you're using, it will have a spectrum within it. I rely on the fact that, if you hit on a good narrative voice without trying, then generally it's going to be doing lots of things naturally because that's the way that we work.

I have to say, this was probably one of the cleanest first drafts I've ever written; the writing of it felt absolutely right. I haven't had that very often, particularly with short stories because they're so tricky.

There was a bit of editing but not much – it just felt really right at the time.

I was probably aware of using the shorter sentences to create tension. Partly this is a folkloric thing because I'm about to try and convince the reader of something inconceivable and to do that there has to be a set of tools. But I don't usually think of writing so mechanically – usually I just work by knowing how to convince.

Because it is quite difficult to believe in some ways, there's an incantatory intonation at the point where she changes into the fox. I always come back to Cormac McCarthy. At the end of *Blood Meridian*, he uses an incantatory tone in order to absolutely terrify the reader. I wanted to use language to get readers into a state where they're ready to receive the idea that this woman has actually turned into a fox.

But also in short stories generally there's a sense of balance that has to be achieved in the language – novels too, but there's a bit more flexibility and variety there perhaps.

Foxes occur often in literature, were you influenced by the folk tale 'Mr Fox' or David Garnett's *Lady into Fox?*

This story is not really a version of *Lady into Fox*, it's more a kind of calque. I knew the plot points in the story; a man has a wife; she turns into a fox; I think in the novella she literally just turns into a fox, there's none of this description of her transformation there. I knew that he feeds her a live bird and tries to live with the fox pups, as well as a strange sense that he still wanted to be married to her.

To me that felt quite subversive on a gender level, the idea that traditionally wives accommodate their husbands and their foibles and ambitions, while the wives are in a supporting role. This reversal felt like the kind of plot I was interested in. I wanted to examine the idea of a man being very loyal to a wife who flexes very far in her remit of who she is. The tragedy of it is she is sort of lost from him in the way a husband or wife might be more literally lost, for example, if they were to walk out or suffer from dementia.

My mum was nursed by my dad when she was terminally ill. This was not something he was brought up and taught to do. I was very interested in this kind of new supporting role for men. I loved the idea of him giving her a live bird in the end because it seemed like such an act of love. It's disgusting to him but he does it anyway.

The ending of mine is very different from *Lady into Fox*. Having not read the novella, it was useful that I was not aware of its language or style so there was no interference with my writing of this.

But I think also it's about a fox because I'm a rural kid. Animals were in the demographic, I don't come from a very ethnically diverse place. Animals were the personalities I was around. I feel like bringing those characters into my work is a fairly natural thing for me.

On the second page you write: 'Of course, this is not the truth.' Why open with a 'false start' like this?

I think it is the truth to recognise that marriages are not necessarily truthful.

In this story there's a lot of double play going on. It is one of its fundamental ideas that people are unknowable, they will alway retain areas that might surprise you. 2020 has been the year of having to live with uncertainty – I think it's one of the big human issues.

The uncertainty of people is something I'm very interested in, the idea that yes they're in love, they have great sex, he adores her, but he still watches pornography.

It's still *pretty* truthful, it's the kind of obvious things that are under the carpet and a short story is all about what's under the carpet.

It seemed like you can't describe the marriage unless we see the discrepancy. We have to recognise this about a couple or else we're not really dealing with the truth. It might seem like a kind of destabilising aspect but I think the recognition of this destabilising is what is vital to the story, because their lives are about to be *completely* destabilised. And not in the way you expect.

The story is rich in many striking themes and details. Did they take many drafts or stages or was this the work of one sitting? With the themes, was it a challenge to know when to be subtle and when explicit?

Initially, I may have had a slightly different ending in mind which worked like a decoy ending as I redrafted and gave me a skewed angle on how things did actually end.

I think as I was writing it, I wrote that last sentence, and thought right, what's my next sentence and realised actually... that's it, that's the ending. This has happened to me a number of times; I'll mentally overshoot the ending, and realise the end has already been achieved.

Sometimes that can produce quite a vertiginous effect. Another short story writer said sometimes my endings created a feeling of vertigo or agoraphobia or they snap shut leaving the reader in the jaws.

I think that's true. Writers can recognise tics or tendencies in their own work. As a writer you want to shake it up and do different things but I think it's fair to say, sometimes you have strengths and sometimes you have ways of communicating that seem to work better.

To answer your question about themes, I remember thinking at the time: *where's this coming from?* Like some of the descriptions about her citrine eyes and her tail like a flaming sceptre. It's possible, because I write visually, at a metaphoric level, I'm not working on metaphors later.

I'm probably the archivist's nightmare because I work over an old draft on the computer so things are lost. The drafts that are printed up are the most helpful because you can see what has been changed, to see the level of thinking – the micro and macro management, line cutting, editing. The writer, Jill Dawson, teaches by showing her drafts and her notes to show her work in progress. Whereas, when I've taken down my scaffolding, I can't remember how I wrote it.

All your points about the Anthropocene's invasive relationship with nature, were they all there in the first draft as well?

Yes, although there was one subtle change. She worked for a real estate company initially, which I added because I wanted to firm up the idea that she herself needed some kind of wildness to break out of her, although at the same time she's working for a company that's rapaciously taking away the land to build houses.

And maybe there are little fact checks along the way. I don't think I realised, for example, that fox shit is scentless. Though hers has an odour to begin with because she is still part-woman.

These things were just a little twist of the reality dial because if you're told something like that by an author then it sounds like they have authority. The expression that's always used in reviews is 'the compelling voice' and I was aiming to give the reader the sense that they are going to be convinced that he is living with a fox.

Cormac McCarthy persuades because he has that sense of occupationalism – I believe he can mend cars because his characters can – the sense that I'm not just a writer making shit up but someone who knows this information, which is very useful if you want to create an authentic world to place the reader in.

Although you were literally making shit up with your description of fox poo.

Yes, there I was making shit up.

How much did you want to make a point about male-female relationships here? Did you have a sense of the balance you

wanted to strike between describing a particular couple and allowing the reader to apply the themes more generally?

I didn't quite realise at the time what I'd done with this story. I've had so many letters from people saying: 'my partner has left me or walked out on me. I couldn't understand it, but this story has allowed me to live with not understanding it'. Or others saying: 'I nursed my partner through an illness and watched their identity dissolving them to become a creature'.

It's such an intimate vulnerable area, the marriage, you choose to form a kind of union, to face the world together until something breaks down or changes – it's an incredible strike to the heart.

The story gets into that intimate place that people have of feeling secure with someone, so there was a sense that their marriage was a series of balances to be manipulated.

He does maintain his love in many ways. He has to accommodate a new version of it for his wife but it's still there. He goes after them, into the woods and, though he can't be a father to these kids, in a way he loves the fox more for what she is. And that's the question at the end of the story: what would the world be like without his wife who doesn't belong to him anymore? Has he let her go? Is that the form of love? I think the answer is unknowable.

But definitely the gender thing is interesting to me – this is a question about our capacities, both men and women. There are incapacities for Mrs Fox – she cannot stay in her marriage, something outside of her control has taken her away from it. There is no indication that she loves her husband. Maybe she allows him to see her cubs but we don't know what that strange feral thing is.

Definitely on the gender level there was some enquiring going on and, as the levels are messed with, it becomes very interesting territory.

I didn't realise what I'd done

I wonder if with the organic way the story came to you, and the strength of readers' reactions might suggest this story touches on something folkloric and universal in us all?

Maybe yes, I suppose it's quite a simple idea. It's a big single event and the procedure and the aftermath of the event. In some ways it's a relatively simple story with some high falutin' language inside. There are political and thematic layers which I hope make it multi-dimensional.

And like a lot of folk tales, it is concerning itself with women's behaviour – was this a 're-wilding' of that story type?

The wilder woman has been something difficult to metabolise for society. Looking at folklore across the world, the older, childless spinster – the witch – is there in just about every culture. The story 'M' in *Sudden Traveller* is a version of 'Manananggal' – the story of an old childless woman who goes around aborting foetuses. There are stories everywhere about the power of a childless, wise, subversive woman, not having children being a feminine statement.

The patriarchy needs to warn itself about her.

Exactly.

Jessie Greengrass said a story is a bit like an argument in that you set out your premises and then draw it to a conclusion. I wondered if this was true here? (I feel towards the end you use more broader statements: 'nothing of the past is left...' and 'no man could be ready.')

I feel a story is an enquiry. I have the question about it and I assume the reader has the same question so together we will consider the enquiry with a narrative scenario. We may never find a full and satisfying answer to it but we will have had a companionability in the asking of a question that is in the minds of all of us if we are honest.

I've recently written a piece for the Arvon Foundation in which I made the analogy that a story is like a piece of a river. It might start at that bend and go on to that bend but it's already flowing and it continues to flow. How shallow or deep it is will depend on the author, but within that stretch of river its angles will change hopefully. Hydrodynamics are incredibly difficult to analyse.

In this section of a river there is a world and movement. There's no dam or tidy finish point, because a story has no neat, fixed ending point. The concept of it is longer, deeper and that is the sign of art and of a good writer when you have this unknown multi-dimensional quality.

Why *this* section of river?

It is probably just a feeling. I'm a sensualist. Sensuality in my work is one of the main operating keys. The plot is not a main operating key. It's one of them because you can't have movement or procedure or development without plot. But plot is inherent – you need to shape it eventually but it's not foremost in my mind.

What I do have to have is a feel of the world and its senses so that the reader can step into it and respond to everything. Humans are responsive and tactile. If they can experience the story rather than reading it, that's when you can trigger their imaginations so they are convinced by it.

Once I've got the feeling of the sensuality of the story – that it's going to be strange or erotic or suburban – that is the mood I want to convey. How I convey that is with the sentence, but within the sentence, I ask myself: *is the poetry right? Will the level of language affect people so they can see it or taste or smell it?*

The characters need to feel real within the story, you don't need to create through portraiture in the space of a short story. The reader will bring in their understanding of people, so you need only a few details.

So I'm not exactly choosing the stretch of river but sensing which is the right way to proceed.

When you've mentioned the husband I feel you are a lot more forgiving of him than I was. The theme of control and taming and ownership crops up often in the language, which led me to dislike him for being so slow to recalibrate his relationship. What do you feel about him?

I have sympathies with his dilemma. Part of me admires his loyalty but he did not understand her initially which is one of those things that make people change and disappear.

I don't know how I felt about the ending other than it seemed in some ways he had done his best, though in other ways he'd totally failed. That also seems true of a marriage – in some ways we try to love each other and respond to each other but often can't or fall short.

You're right the language holds tight where she trots up to him 'like she could ever be his pet'. There are these seeds in it: did he want to own her? Was she too constrained? What happens when people are offered more freedom?

These are not overt questions. Is it terrible that the story does not provide answers or a neat ending? I don't know, I don't think so.

Really towards the end he's been brought so far. When someone leaves you, there's a strange undoing of yourself, the reasons for your actions and you have to live with the catastrophe.

But eventually he allows it to exist in its natural state.

What did you learn with the writing of this story?

I haven't looked at the process of writing very much. I can't know it. I've been writing for 25 years but knowing is not that useful for me.

I mostly find it helpful to answer questions when I write, and with this story it felt really successful. The construction of it felt natural which doesn't help. Because there was something sitting behind it, not a shape but an idea. I think I've written stories as good as this but with different methods.

I have learned really successful sentences are not overloaded but are powerful. Generally my work has moved that way. It is still descriptive, still conceptual but now the concept is more integrated with the language.

I was 28 when I wrote *Electric Michaelangelo* and it's loved but it has these stretches of conceptual and descriptive and rhyming language – they're fun and good but now I hope my writing makes better use of all the component parts.

That story was a highlight and I recognise it so I do look back on it but I'm not sure what *exactly* I take from it.

I think I probably sensed the success of the story. There was a sense of failure in my other work which, though still good work, didn't fully achieve what I set out to do. But here I do feel I achieved what I hoped for.

The First Punch

by Jon McGregor

The first punch is a shock. We're taking a short-cut across where the old steelworks used to be, that huge old strip of land between the river and the canal with the motorway flying somewhere way overhead and down here it's almost quiet. Silver birch trees and rowan bushes bursting up through the concrete foundations. Thistles with bright purple flowerheads, stray yellow rapeseed flown in from the fields outside town, those white flowers with the petals like trumpets that wind their way across the ground and up round anything they can get their feelers onto. Butterflies and dragonflies and the evening-song of birds that have lived here for centuries. He says, you wouldn't have thought this was a foundry just five years ago would you. Everywhere there are scattered lumps of machinery, lost cogs and gearwheels, stacks of plate, coils of wire. He says, the way these trees come back you wouldn't believe it. He was one of the last workers to be laid off here, and he can still point out where the steel was smelted and poured and formed; the outlines of the old sheds and foundry-halls spread out across the whole site like a giant blueprint, ankle-high walls rearing up to hold a tall window frame, a door hanging off its hinges. But mostly there are trees and bushes and birdlife, and it's a good place to walk on a long summer's evening with the sky stretching hazy blue over our heads, a couple of pints swimming through us and one or other of us talking quietly now and again.

So when the first punch comes, it's a shock. Straight into my stomach and my body folds around it, the breath knocked out of me and I stagger backwards with my feet scraping and scrabbling on the stony ground. Perhaps it doesn't make sense that I'm surprised, because why else would we be out here, talking about these things, all this talk of I love my wife and if anyone ever tried I know what I'd do, but as I drag the air back into my winded lungs I'm surprised and I don't understand.

I look up at him, laughing, as though it might be a joke or I can somehow turn it into one, and I say what what are you doing what's this? He brings the heel of his open hand crashing into the side of my head like a lump-hammer. I almost fall to the ground, and there's a high-pitched ringing noise in my ears and I can't think and I don't know how to respond. I lift my arms up around my head, turning away, and he pulls my wrists to my side as he slams his forehead into the bridge of my nose.

I'm on the ground, and he is standing over me. Everything is muffled. I'm aware of the sound of running water somewhere. He stoops over me, and punches each side of my head alternately, each punch knocking my head across to meet the next. My arms reach up again to shield myself, but he just punches on through them. He is breathing heavily, watching me, concentrating.

When he stops, there is pain. A hot roar of pain flooding through me. I turn my head to one side and vomit onto the ground. He stands away slightly, getting his breath back.

And this is not right. I should be running away, or defending myself, or calling for help, but I am doing none of these things. I am lying on the dirty ground, watching him, waiting for his next move.

He says what did you think you were doing?

He says how did you even imagine you were going to get away with it?

The First Punch

He calls me a cunt, and he kicks me in the side, his boot fitting neatly between my hip bone and the base of my ribcage.

===================

The first time she ever touched me, she touched me on the back of the head, her fingers trailing down through my hair to the nape of my neck, up again, down again, suddenly pulling away as though scorched against a hotplate. She said sorry sorry and for some reason I said sorry too and we didn't say anything else about it. But the way it felt; her long fingers pressing lightly and firmly, the slight scratch of her fingernails. I could feel the lines they had traced across my scalp, tingling.

It had come from nowhere, a lull in the conversation, her hand drifting there with her eyes fixed firmly on mine and I didn't pull away or say anything to stop her, and afterwards I wanted her to do it again and I wanted to leave and I wanted her not to have done it.

We were sitting in the park. We'd finished our lunches and were about to go back to work, back to our different offices in the same building and I can't even think now how it was we'd first come across each other and started talking the way we did. I was thinking about the cases I'd be dealing with that afternoon and suddenly there were her fingers trailing down the back of my neck and she was touching me.

I don't know how we got to that. I've never been clear how anyone ever gets to that.

A few moments later she said excuse me but you just looked a bit sad. I said did I? and she said kind of wistful and I said oh I was just thinking about work and she laughed. That laugh.

She was younger than me, about ten years younger I think but I never really noticed. It never seemed important, meeting for lunch and drinks after work and sometimes being on the same bus. It was only ever about conversation. Our ages, or the rings we both wore, were nothing to do with any of it. We were good at talking to each other was all it was. I could tell her about work, and Eleanor, and fatherhood, and I wouldn't feel like she wanted me to stop. She could tell me about her job, and her husband, and his job, and all the things she liked and didn't like about her life, and I wouldn't feel like there was anything I needed to say. Sometimes our conversation was funny, sometimes it was patient and sad, but always it just came easily and kept on going. And I thought I believed that the sheer startling fact of her physical beauty was no part of the way I enjoyed her company. But the way it felt, that day in the park when she just ran her fingers down through the hair on the back of my head, that was something; and her voice saying because she thought I looked like I was feeling sad, that was something more again.

It had been a long time since anyone had done that.

I wanted to say thankyou but instead I said sorry. She laughed, and she said you look good when you're thinking, pretty. I was embarrassed for a moment. Pretty seemed like a strange word to use of a forty-year old man with lines around his eyes.

But all that happened next was I looked at my watch and stood up to go back to work. She said have a good afternoon, I walked away, and when I turned back to look she wasn't looking at me. She was reading something, running her fingers up and down the back of her head, through her dark tangle of hair. I went back to work, and I tried not to think about it, and the next time I saw her was that afternoon at her house. His house.

——————

He comes towards me, and my body tenses, my forearms crossing over my face. He crouches beside me, and pulls my arms away, pinning them to my chest with one hand. I look at him. His eyes are wide and clear, he is sweating a little, there are strands of hair sticking to his forehead. He takes off his jacket, rolls it up, and puts it under my head for a pillow. He doesn't say a word. I look at him, my vision still clouded, my mouth gaping soundlessly. He smiles.

I say, but but what but I didn't do anything.

He smiles again. He says you loved it didn't you?

I look at him, and I don't know what to say. I say, I didn't, what? no, no I didn't.

He winces, turns away, turns back. You fucking liar he says, don't fucking lie to me.

The memory of her. Standing there in that dress. Her bare shoulders and the way she looked at me with those eyes. The movement of the dress when she turned in the doorway, the way it swung around the backs of her legs. That was all it took; her looking at me like that, those eyes, the way the dress swung around the backs of her long bare legs as she turned in the doorway there.

He rushes in towards me and stamps his foot down onto my chest and again all the breath is forced out of me, again there is staggering sickening pain. He does this three times, and the third time, barely realising what I am doing, I roll over and start to crawl away, scraping my hands on the brambles, heading towards the sound of rushing water. I can hear shouted voices somewhere, and laughter. I am crawling for perhaps thirty seconds when I hear quick footsteps behind me and feel a sudden snapping impact to the back of my head. I stop crawling.

He rolls me over, onto my back, and places the pillow beneath my head again, looking down at me with a look on his face as if he wants me to speak. I am shivering. My breathing is ragged and torn. I can hear the shouted voices from somewhere over by the river, I can see the cars rushing across the flyover way up in the sky.

He says don't fucking lie to me David.

He says I don't need people lying to me, I won't have it, I need to be able to trust people, it's not much to ask is it?

I look at him. He takes out a packet of cigarettes, putting the pack to his mouth and biting one out like a splinter from a hand. He puts the packet back and lights the cigarette.

He says she's my wife yeah? I know what she looks like, I know what happens when she's wearing that dress, I know what it does to the way she looks yeah? I bought her that dress so that she'd look like that, he says. I don't know what I'm supposed to say, I watch him and I keep breathing and I listen to the sound of the voices somewhere getting quieter now.

He says and you're telling me you were in the house with her, in the middle of the afternoon, and she's wearing that dress, and you didn't even want to?

He calls me a liar again, he comes closer and he looks at me and he smokes his cigarette.

The second time she ever touched me was that afternoon in her house. I can't quite remember why I was there, she'd asked me to pop round and help move a sofa or a table or something but when I got there she didn't mention it. It was a hot day, she had her hair all tied up on top of her head and wisps of it were falling out, she kept tucking them behind her ear, fanning herself with a piece of paper and saying hey I'm hot aren't you? And every time she said it she giggled, nervously or embarrassedly or excitedly I couldn't tell. She had a laugh that made my ears flush red. He was out at work, she told me that, more than once.

She poured us both a cold drink, orange juice with lemonade, and she dropped ice-cubes into the glasses. She dared me to suck a whole ice-cube and I dared her back, and we stood there in her kitchen with our mouths puckered around a block of ice each, grimacing at each other, her eyes watering and sparkling, and when she spat hers out and laughed and leaned towards me that was the second time she touched me. Her two hands flat to my chest, gently, briefly.

It had been a long time since anyone had done that.

It was a blue dress she was wearing, pale blue as though it had been washed too often, and it hung from her bare round shoulders on straps as thin as parcel string. It was cut into a sort of v at the back, and when she turned and reached up to a shelf, leaning back slightly, I could see almost down to her waist before I looked away.

We sat in the front room with our cold drinks. She sat beside me, not close enough to touch but turned towards me with her legs folded beneath her and one arm laid out along the back of the sofa. And she talked a lot, quickly, she laughed and the way she laughed made me feel uncomfortable and good at the same time. And when she didn't talk she took a long slow sip of her drink, looking over me at the top of her glass, a long slow look which I wanted to look away from but couldn't.

She asked me how were things with Eleanor, and I said the same, that she wasn't spending so long in bed but that she still wouldn't leave the house and she still looked puffy-eyed when I came in from work. I told her the doctor had been talking about a different medication and that I wasn't sure that was really the answer. This was almost a routine conversation by now. She said it's good you know, what you do for her, I respect that, and I said no, really, I mean she's my wife what else would I do?

She was wearing a long bead necklace, she was twisting it between two fingers and when she let it go it fell against bare skin.

She said I'm glad you're here it's good to have you here and I said well it's good to be here and I was being mock polite but really I meant it. It was good to be there, on her sofa, with a cold drink, her sitting with me, in that dress, tucking wisps of dark hair behind her ear and talking and laughing. She said is it?, suddenly, demandingly, is it good to be here, are you glad you're here? And I said yes, yes it is, yes I am, and I was confused and she was quiet.

I finished my drink. I went to the toilet. I washed my face and my hands, and when I came out of the bathroom at the top of the stairs that was when it happened.

She was standing in the open doorway of the room next to the bathroom, leaning against the doorframe slightly, she'd taken her shoes off and she had one ankle curled round behind the other.

The blue dress hung down to her knees, but with one leg lifted like that it rode up a little, about a third way up her thigh.

I looked at her.

That was all. I just looked at her.

She lifted a hand to adjust the knot of hair at the back of her head, and smiled.

And that could have been enough, that moment, standing there looking at her, and her smile, for me, that hot day with the windows open and the sleepy sounds of summer drifting through the house, a lawnmower somewhere, children shouting.

She said how do I look? and it seemed like she really wanted to know, standing there beautiful and desirable every inch of her, like she wasn't sure, her elegant bare feet and the smooth straight rise of her legs, the way her dress pulled against the curve of her hips and the press of her breasts, her shoulders, her neck, her eyes. Her eyes looked strange for a moment, when I looked, anxious almost. I said you look good and she said do I? really? as if she wasn't sure, as if she thought I might be humouring her somehow, as if there was no-one who told her each day how good she looked. I said, very quietly, yes you do, you look very good. She smiled again, looking away for a moment, looking over her shoulder into the room. I still hadn't moved. When she turned back her eyes looked different and she wasn't smiling. She said, quietly, looking straight at me, do you want me? I did. I wanted her. Hugely and deeply I wanted her. I said, I whispered, yes. She said, her voice quiet and unsteady, oh good, and she turned quickly in the doorway, stepping into the room, out of sight. I didn't even breathe.

That movement, the turn of her hips, the swing and lift of her dress, the backs of her legs.

I don't know how long she waited. I didn't move. I couldn't. She reappeared, and when she spoke this time her eyes spilled clearly over into tears, her voice cracking. She said don't be shy I'm waiting for you. She said don't you want me you said you wanted me. I said I do. She said well come on then, and she opened her mouth slightly, and there were tears down both her cheeks, shining. I wanted her incredibly. I hesitated. I turned and walked down the stairs, out into the afternoon sunshine.

———————

My hands are folded together on my chest, I am having trouble breathing and the pain is everywhere now. He looks at me. His cigarette is halfway to the filter. He coughs a little, turning to spit on the ground. He says excuse me, sorry.

He walks towards me and crouches down. He says, listen, you and Eleanor, that's your problem.

He says I don't care if she's not giving you any. I don't give a shit if she makes you sleep in the spare room or if she never even wants to undress in front of you again. I'm not bothered. It's got nothing to do with me. But you're not having mine, alright? He says it very quietly, smiling, as though he's trying not to laugh, and he stands up.

I didn't tell him anything about Eleanor. He shouldn't know all that. I've only ever talked to one person about these things.

He taps the end of his cigarette, and flakes of ash flutter to the ground. He says I'm sorry about all this mate, but it had to be done. He says you got to be able to trust people David, else what's the point?

He says I'm not having you or no-one fucking about with that, alright?

He flicks his cigarette away and looks at me for a few moments, as if he's waiting for me to say something in return. There is nothing I can say.

He turns and walks away from me, heading towards the bridge over the river where the footpath leads to the steps up the side of the hill, through the woods and out into the streets to the house where he lives with his wife.

I watch until he disappears amongst the trees and the bushes. I stand up, slowly and painfully. The sun is low in the sky, everything is bright and clear and peaceful and I feel sick. Dizzy. Confused.

I start to make my way home. It feels like a long way. As soon as I start walking I have to stop for a moment, my breath caught tight in my bruised lungs.

The cars rush across the flyover. Birds crowd together overhead, sweeping across the sky. Dandelions and thistles and blackberry bushes force their way up through the broken concrete.

I walk towards the bridge, towards the steps up the side of the hill and the house where I live with my pale and tearful wife. I will ask her how she is. I will fetch her what she needs from the kitchen. I will take her to the bathroom. She trusts me to do this for her. It's important. You have to be able to trust people.

The Prevaricative Voice

Jon McGregor on The First Punch

In November 2003, when this story was published in Granta, Jon McGregor was a 27-year-old debut novelist. He is now in his forties, winner of the Costa Book Award 2017 and a Professor of Creative Writing at the University of Nottingham.

Reading his earlier work now, we talked about what he liked in the story and what he had learnt since.

Can you remember your first inspiration for this story or what moved you to write it?

I think I must have written it after my first novel was published, which was 2002.

This one had been a kind of exercise for me in writing a story that would have a really simple premise, and be easy to describe to someone. I'd got really fed up trying to describe *If Nobody Speaks Of Remarkable Things* to people because it is essentially a novel where not much happens – it's mostly about some people sitting around and that's about it.

With this I wanted to write about a man who gets beaten up. It was an exercise in letting action lead a story, which seems like an obvious thing to do but at that point definitely wasn't my starting point for writing a piece of fiction and still isn't my starting point.

So I started off with the idea of a man getting beaten up and I guess I worked outwards from there – why does he get beaten up? Who is beating him up? What's the connection between them? Where's it happening? And from these questions a lot of other ideas occurred.

This might be too sweeping a generalisation but are your short stories more action-packed than your novels?

Possibly. I've certainly started off a short story with a much greater idea of what would happen if I tried to do x or y or z. Sometimes that's about the form and sometimes that's about the story itself.

My latest novel, *Lean Fall Stand* [published April 2021] definitely has more action and more drama after I experienced quite a turning point.

I wrote some stories [*The Reservoir Tapes*] for Radio 4 a couple of years ago that were a follow up to *Reservoir 13*. The producers and I were really clear that with a piece of radio fiction you have to get and hold people's attention. I had an image in my mind of someone accidentally catching the first couple of sentences of the story because they were listening to whatever was on beforehand. I needed to think what I would do to hold their attention when they weren't expecting to listen to a story and it kind of forced me to do the things you're supposed to do with fiction and drama: thinking about what happened and what makes the reader curious and what's going to hold their attention.

It was quite an eye opener for me.

When writing 'The First Punch', I saw that the scene itself was inherently dramatic but I was telling it from the point of view of someone remembering it twenty years later. I suddenly thought, why am I doing that? Why not go back and tell the story *at that moment*.

I think I've always had an instinct for being slow and

reflective and thoughtful about storytelling when actually you can make a story much more interesting by getting to the point and staying on the point.

Once you had found the simple premise of the punch, and explored the background to this, what do you think of the direction you gave the story?

The one thing that really struck me re-reading it was I had forgotten that he doesn't sleep with the woman – he doesn't do what he's getting beaten up for.

At first, I was kind of amused that my younger self was such a prude or so naive to think in that situation he would turn around and walk away but it is also interesting that the betrayal of trust is her lying to her husband out of her sense of rejection. There is a lot that I would critique about that story from a technical point of view but the nuts and bolts of it I am reasonably happy with, in that in a story you always want an extra layer of unexpectedness.

George Saunders has written really well on what he wants a story to do. There's an essay of his I use a lot when I'm teaching, about a Donald Barthelme story ['The Perfect Gerbil: Reading Donald Barthelme's The School', from *The Braindead Megaphone* (Bloomsbury)]. Saunders talks about how you want the ending to do more than you thought it would do; how the structure is almost like a joke in that you need a punchline but not necessarily a funny one.

In this story the reader's first question is why is this person getting beaten up? Then we find out about the woman which makes the reader assume the reason and then the reason turns out to be something else altogether. So I'd give my younger self good marks for that.

Although there are other technical aspects that I'd revisit.

What are these technical aspects?

There's some surface level stuff about punctuation and

syntax and commas that made me wince a little bit. I think at that stage in my writing I was partly attempting to be very free and liberated and experimental in my use of punctuation but I think I did not have an adequate technical grasp of how to use commas and semicolons.

It's fine to not use speech marks for speech but at least work out how you're going to frame it in a sentence. There's lots of stuff like that that I would like to tidy up but there's also a thing that I quite often find myself now picking up students for. Do you know Chris Power?

Yes, I recently interviewed him.

Oh ok, brilliant, well the first time I met him, I had asked to talk to him about a really interesting review of his about my collection of short stories in 2012 [*This Isn't the Sort of Thing That Happens to Someone Like You*]. This story wasn't in that collection, but a lot of those stories were written about that period. He'd written a review that was kind of mixed in a really interesting way. I wanted to talk to him more about that and what he felt I could do. He was saying some of these stories were better than others and I was really interested to know why.

Did you have him up against a wall when you were asking this?

No, I think I bought him brunch. He's written for years for *The Guardian* about short stories and he's clearly someone who understands the form really well. One of the things he pointed out to me was what he called the prevaricative voice, a tendency he sees in a lot of short story writing.

He showed me lots of places where I was prevaricating – where I said it 'was sort of like this *and also* like that' or 'I can't quite remember why.' I was being evasive very deliberately – I thought it was to do with the slipperiness of memory and the imprecision of observation and the way that often we're not sure, but actually it comes across as a bit of a tic. It has an artificiality about it.

The narrator says: 'I can't even think now how it was we'd first come across each other,' and 'She was ten years younger I think but I never really noticed.' Looking at it now after those conversations with Chris about prevarication, it just seems a bit woolly and unnecessary. If a narrator is going to the trouble of recalling a story why would they be so imprecise about that part. Yes, memory is imprecise but generally your brain attempts a singular version.

So you would fill in the gaps if you were to write this now?

Yeah, that and the commas.

But there are also some very effective things going on here – for example I wondered to what degree you made the dilapidated industrial setting reflect or at least correspond to the action.

I'm not sure I was being that clever. I think I was interested in the social distance between the two of them – looking at it now, I think that was a bit clumsy. I think all three of them are slightly clumsily drawn in terms of their personas and social positions. I was definitely interested in the narrator being somebody who works in an office and has a vaguely middle class background and the other guy being someone who used to be an ex-steel worker, someone's whose job and sense of identity and sense of purpose has been lost.

At the time, and still now, I'm really interested in those post-industrial landscapes in the socio-economic sense, this whole generation of men growing up expecting to have this role in their life, but when that vanishes and they have to learn new ways of being men and are not equipped for it, having not had the conversation about what *are* the new ways of being a man.

I lived in Sheffield not long before I wrote this story and its setting is very vivid for me, specifically a piece of land to the

east, between Sheffield and Rotherham – the Rother valley –
that used to be miles and miles of enormous steel works, but at
that point at the very end of last century was a huge wasteland
and quite a pleasant place to be from a nature lover's perspective.

I think I was using this setting to allow the guy to mention
he'd been a steel worker and wasn't now. I was interested in an
incident like this happening in that kind of edgeland landscape,
out of sight but I don't think I was trying to marry the urban
wasteland aggression and violence in that specific way.

**You spoke earlier about the purposelessness in the story – I
wondered if the mood felt all very much part of a piece with
the prevarication? For example, with the foundry shutting
down, in the woman's attempt to get the protagonist into
bed, it felt as if they were all shattered by the aftermath of
something. Didn't the prevarication suit the story quite well?**

I suspect that *some* of that vagueness was their lack of drive
but I think if I were writing that story now I would probably be
looking for a bit more oomph. A bit more information about who
she is, where they work, how they know each other.

**But without that conventional information it puts the story
on an odd and unsettling plain. It's eerie that the protagonist
is out walking with this guy whose wife he nearly slept with.
I would have thought he would be more wary. Nor do I fully
believe her courting of this 'pretty' forty-year-old. For me
the vagueness and the fact that this is not obviously realistic
comes across as an important part of the story.**

That's good. At that stage of my writing I was really
interested in images and moods and sensation and feeling and
not so interested in character and motivation and plot and logic.

I think I can look back at that now and I can remember that I
thought those three characters were completely realistic and the
story was realistic and did hold together and I don't think it does

– I think it exists at this other level that you're talking about – the level of mood or symbol or representation.

I was going to ask you about the aggressor. Some of the things he says and does seem slightly stilted, like the way he props up the protagonist's head with the coat before returning to his attack. Can you remember what the thinking was there?

Not really no, this was an experiment in what would it be like to write about action and violence and those were my attempts. School was the last time I experienced physical violence and aggression so I was operating in the dark a little bit. Certainly, reading it now, some of his dialogue feels clumsy and as if trying to sound like Ray Winston, or going a bit too far in that direction.

Can you remember much about your process? For example, were there many drafts?

I think I know at that time I was writing first drafts longhand, only typing them up to print them out and rework them.

That parallel structure of the scene in the waste ground with flashbacks to being at her house, I suspect I landed on that quite early because it is a kind of a similar structure to the one I used in my first novel. It's a really straightforward structure, a really easy way to generate a bit of pace, cutting back and forth like that.

I imagine I played around a lot with how long to stay with one strand before cutting back to the other. There would have been quite a lot of paring back but probably not as much as in later short stories, where I know I did that a lot more. It was still very early in my writing career and I didn't know what I was doing.

Looking at it now, I guess this is the weakest part of the story – the friendship between him and this guy how it was they had been for a drink and gone for a walk. I hope when that scene was rewritten in the novel it made more sense – the weakness of this story is that work hasn't been done yet.

Where you would use the word 'weaknesses' I would use the word 'ambiguity'. You don't think the younger self was aiming for that?

Yes, I think my younger self was a big fan of ambiguity and I think Chris Power has won me round to the idea that ambiguity is an excuse for vagueness. When I was younger I was very clever at getting away with having only a vague sense of what the story was and turning that into ambiguity. Which is a neat trick for a while but eventually it gets old.

Looking back on this now, what did you like in the story? What skills and strengths did you notice in the story's youthful author?

I was pleasantly surprised by some of the key images. That first moment of violence, the imagery of it still feels quite vivid to me. And the small moments of body language and pauses, those are the kind of things that I started doing quite early in my writing.

Thinking about two people in a space and all the stuff that's happening underneath and before the dialogue. I've always found dialogue really difficult so I've always focused on the other stuff.

I landed on that early in my writing. I think it's something I have an instinct for. There's a lot in this story that I wouldn't chuck away.

I think that premise of the misunderstanding between the three of them and the fact he's getting beaten up for something he didn't do, the complication of that, is something I think that holds up as an interesting mechanic for a short story.

You were a young man writing about a forty-year-old. What do you think of the author's portrayal of marriage and life in middle age? I wondered whether, now you're much nearer the age of the protagonist, are there shifts in how you see the story?

The Prevaricative Voice

There's a line quite early on where he speaks about having lines around his eyes. Clearly when I was in my mid-twenties that was the key marker that when you hit forty you start wrinkling. This is another thing I have noticed with students – this weird sense that anyone above 22 is just 'old' and there's no distinguishing features within that.

It says she's ten years younger than him which makes her 30 and we're supposed to think her husband is the same age but there's again a kind of vagueness – the protagonist being a 'middle-aged guy', there's not quite enough there. I was writing him just as 'old guy.'

Once I hit forty I didn't feel that old, just slightly more tired. I think that's the big challenge with writing and the one thing I keep talking to students about: the need to avoid making people into types and hiving characters off as older or middle aged.

There's a real tendency to write about 'the businessman' or 'the homeless man' or 'the jogger' – the business man wears a suit and doesn't give money to the homeless, but I would ask, who *is* this guy? What *is* his actual job? Was that the job he wanted to do when he left school? At the weekends does he build a model railway or go clubbing?

I try to force people to think – here it seems the only thinking I did was to know he worked in an office. It would have been more interesting to push the details.

Though, would too much reality pop the bubble the story exists in?

Yeah, potentially you've also got to be careful about how much information you pack into a story. But the fact that I still have no idea what that office was shows that I didn't do that thinking.

The Hemingway nonsense about the iceberg is a little bit suspect and a little bit magical thinking but the more details you know about a character the more precise you can make them appear.

Every time I've read the story a different dynamic seems to be at its heart. Which again is maybe part of its 'swimmingness' and its ambiguity? Each relationship the reader latches onto proves not fully dependable, and doesn't quite form the core of the story, which maybe points to a deeper level of resonance... For you is there one relationship at the heart of the story?

One of the things that struck me on re-reading was that the relationship of the narrator and his wife comes completely into focus in that last paragraph. I hope the reader gleans he didn't sleep with the woman because of how he feels about his wife. That was one of things I was trying to do with the ending, to take something that seemed to be about this over here and bring the reader's attention over there.

The relationship between him and the woman, the almost completely unseen relationship between her and this guy and the conversations we assume have taken place – and that relationship, the slight edge of desperation and whether he wants her and what that implies about their relationship and also the friendship – I don't think any one of these is *the* focus – the story is about shifting reader's attention between those different relationships.

Hair

by Mahreen Sohail

The boy's mother is sick and has lost all her hair. In solidarity, he decides to cut his off too. He thinks this is the least a son can do for a sick mother. The first person he tells is his girlfriend of one year. I'm going to donate my hair to my mother, he says, and is worried to see tears rise in her eyes. She had told him soon after they met that the first thing she liked about him was his shoulder-length hair, how it lay wild and free on top of his head, caused people on the street to glance back at them when they walked anywhere together. The boy worries that she is actually horrified at the idea of him cutting off his hair. *But it's my mother*, he thinks to himself, *it's my choice*. Before he can make a case the girl, a nice girl from a middle-class family who knows how to drop meaningful hints coyly (my parents are looking for a boy for me) finally says, I think cutting your hair for aunty would be a wonderful thing to do.

The mother is in bed with the smooth baldness of her newly shaved scalp, a scarf loosely draped across her neck. She does not know her son has gone to donate his hair, and is not the sort of mother who would approve if she did know. She does not believe one person being ill is the reason for another to act ill. And anyway, if she did know, she would have had enough faith in the girl to stop her son. She likes the girl. She thinks she is a good choice for her son, and maybe in a few years they will marry but the mother does not know if she will be alive for the wedding. A pure-cut line of steel runs through the mother and she knows the world moves on and on, so there is no need for theatrics, no need really for anything while she is so tired and in bed, staring up at the ceiling for hours on end, something she has only recently discovered is strangely meditative. Odd now to think that when her husband built the house she found the textured cream paint a little creepy, even said so to him then, The texture is a little creepy, a statement which the husband in his usual overbearing style, overrode. But now she understands why he chose the paint, maybe. It's easy for her to fall asleep while trying to follow the pattern it makes on the ceiling.

The salon is unisex. The boy and girl unclasp their hands when they enter and the boy explains at the counter what he wants. He says, I want to make sure my hair can be donated. His hair is tied up in the usual bun and he loosens it when he talks so the curls fall to his shoulders. I want it to be a wig for my mother. The woman behind the counter calls her associate's name and they descend on the boy and touch his head gently, with some sadness, as if he is their pet and they are about to say goodbye. Behind them, the girl stands with her own long, straight hair shining down her back, almost down to her knees. She rubs her arms as if she is cold, feels herself rising to the middle of this story and floating in the very center of it.

The husband watches the wife sleep. The house is nicest whenever she is asleep because he worries less about her and knows for a fact that she is resting, and for a little while at least he manages to forget that she is dying. This is more bearable than watching her lie awake and worry about dying. The husband is unsure if he has loved anyone in his life, at least in the way he thought he would love when he was younger, but now he thinks that maybe this is what love is supposed to be; you build a life around a person and when they threaten to go, you worry and worry that they will take you with them. If this is it, then he would prefer to go back to being a stranger to his wife.

The hairdresser winds his fingers through the boy's hair. He stretches out the curls, wets them with a spray bottle and combs through the hair with his fingers again. The boy looks at the man's face. Will it be possible? he asks. The man tries hard to look matter-of-fact, I'm sorry, he says, your hair has to be at least twelve inches long when the length is taken from the nape of your neck.

The girl feels her heart squeeze. The thing is – the thing is, she knows already that she wants to be with the boy, and while mostly her heart is compassionate for his family, some part of her is also thinking about how to make sure the boy will stay with her, *This is my time*, she thinks. The boy is nineteen years old this year, and like most nineteen-year-old boys seems not to know what he is doing and the girl is worried. She is eighteen, almost nineteen, and most of her friends are dating the men they believe they will marry. *Surely a man she is here for right now in the most impossible moment of his life will want her by his side forever*, the girl thinks. She rearranges her face so that it resembles a scissor, like something about to cut herself or the boy, and says, I'll do it. The boy looks at the girl's hair and says, You don't have to do this, but it is weak. They switch chairs and the hairdresser is swishing the towel around the girl's neck and spraying her hair with water and tying it in a ponytail at the nape of her neck.

Are you ready? he asks and she nods. Then he cuts it all off in two quick strokes. She closes her eyes for a second, but really she feels like a saint. She feels quite amazing, as if she has finally transcended petty relationships and is now in the midst of the truest, greatest love she is capable of.

The watching boy realises he has made a big mistake. She looks terrible.

The wife does not open her eyes even though she feels she must get up soon to cook. She drifts in and out of consciousness during the day and the night, which the doctor had said was quite common at their last appointment, but even so it is easy to imagine that she will be better after this day passes. Maybe even in a few moments. I would love daal chawal, she says sleepily, actually wanting to get up and make it herself but her husband sitting by her side stands quickly. If you'll just go back to sleep, he pleads, I'll make it for you. He heads to the kitchen and pulls down the lentils from the top cupboard, pulls out the rice and looks at the two things for a moment. He wishes for a second that his son was home. It would be so lovely to have him here, both of them healthy and men, which sometimes feels like the natural order of things or if not the natural order of things at least some order of things.

The girl feels freer with the short hair. The hairdresser has not let the cut hair fall to the ground. He is still holding it in his fist so it descends like a black ribbon toward the floor. It can't touch the floor, he says, that's a no-no for wigs. We'll send it away and they'll mail you the wig in a week. The girl looks in the mirror at the boy's face and he seems ashen, absolutely wrecked, and again the girl feels triumphant. *This is it*, she thinks, *what a small sacrifice for him to fall in love with me!* The girl bargains in her head all the time about the boy – *if I do this he will do that, and if I do that he will do this* – so sometimes it can feel like he is lodged like a small, sharp rock in her head. The haircut has made his presence in her head lighter, as if a little bit of him has also been cut away with her hair.

The hairdresser puts the hair on a shelf, labels it with the boy's mother's name and he comes back to the girl. Her hair looks uneven. Would you like a bob-cut? he asks and she says, Sure. Riding on her high, she decides to try something fun. She gets an asymmetrical bob with the longer side touching her chin and the other side riding up to her ear. She does look a little experimental, like someone who could break up with the boy now, like she could live alone for a few years. The hairdresser asks if he can take a picture of her and she says, Yes, so he takes the towel off and swivels her around and uses a phone to take a picture. You'll find this online by this evening, he says and the girl beams. The girl and the boy hold hands out of the salon, their path lit up by the smiles of the salon staff.

Actually, the boy's hand feels like it is crawling with ants. These ants are coming out of his pores to protest. The girl looks horrible, he thinks, and he remembers how last night he had kissed her on her stomach and her back had arched a little off the bed and when it did her hair had lain thick under her, half on the mattress and half stuck to her spine, where he had brushed it off carelessly. The thing is the boy knows it is a terrible thing to like people based on their looks, and she is an amazing person. Which is worse, he wonders, to like someone less because they are ugly, or because they have become better than you during what is supposed to be the most character-building, mother-losing year of your life?

He decides while they drive home and as he takes sidelong glances at her, that he could like it more if it was a symmetrical bob. As if on cue she asks, Do you think it's too experimental?

The mother wakes and through a haze she can see her son and her husband and the girl standing there. The girl looks younger somehow. The husband is holding an entire plate of food and the smell of the food makes the mother sick. She turns on her side and vomits. I don't think your mother likes my hair, the girl says.

It looks great, the boy's father tells the girl, still holding the plate. Yes, the boy lies, it does. All three of them reach for the wastepaper basket filled with the vomit but none of them actually touch it. The mother pants, spent, on the bed.

That night the boy drives the girl back to her house. The maid opens the main door and avoids looking at the boy. The house staff is supposed to pretend the girl is pure and does not do anything with the boy except go out to public places and eat.

The girl's parents pretend this too, or at least the mother does, and later she tells the girl's father, She will never get married if we keep her locked up in the house. Things have changed, and our daughter knows her limits.

The boy says hello to the girl's mother who is standing near the kitchen and the mother says hello back normally, but then her gaze falls on her daughter and she lets out a small scream, What did you do? The girl hesitates for a second, then speaks quickly, shyly, His mother needed a wig, and the mother, who is smart, understands why the daughter has done this, tries to redo her reaction so that she seems proud to have a daughter who can give this sort of sacrifice for the man she wants to be with, but really, the mother also feels immeasurably sad. All that long, beautiful hair.

The girl's hair is sent to a wig-maker in the middle of the city who threads each strand so it bands together again, coheres into a new shape for the recipient. The wig-maker reads the file of the recipient of the wig: 62; HOUSEWIFE. *Sixty-two-year-olds like layers in their hair*, he thinks so he cuts in a few layers and then gently puts the wig in crêpe paper, lays it down in a wooden box filled with small spheres of styrofoam. He tapes the box shut and presses on the address label.

The next day the boy kisses the girl on the lips when she is visiting his house. How's your mother? she asks when they are alone in his room and he says, Good, and then he kisses her again. When he puts his face near the side of the bob that is shorter, he feels as if something is missing, as if he is going out with a person without a limb.

I love this, he says and keeps kissing her, kisses her neck, easier to reach now, and she leans up and kisses him back. His parents are asleep in the other room so she bites his shoulder to keep from crying out during sex. Later when she sleeps, her shoulders and neck remain damp. He quietly gets out of bed and he takes scissors from his drawer. She is turned onto the side of her face with the shorter hair length. He lifts the longer hair from off her face and cuts it, taking care to hold the cut strands so they don't fall back on her face and wake her. The moment he cuts her hair he feels that deep satisfaction that only comes from having made something even again. She does look slightly better, though he's done a messy job. *This is fine*, he thinks, *it will grow back*. He throws the hair he has cut into the bin.

After throwing out the hair, the boy goes to his parents' room. The two of them are playing cards, though the mother has to be prompted to make a move by the father. Your turn, the father says every few minutes and the mother stares at him blankly before saying, Oh yes, and concentrating hard on the hand that she has been dealt. *Okay*, the boy thinks sitting on the bed with his parents, *They're fine*.

How is the girl? the father asks and the boy says, Good, good, good, three times in quick succession. He leaves to go back and watch the girl sleep.

Is this how sociopaths behave? He thinks about this while she is asleep and wonders if he could kill her if he had to and he thinks the answer is no, though you never know how you will react to things. This is the first girl he has ever slept with and he has cut her hair without permission. Who knows what else is inside him: a person who beats up women, a person who actually wants his mother to die now, a person who often wakes up thinking enough is enough.

The girl wakes and flies at him. She is ready to kill him: Are You Insane? and the father comes running: Why are you disturbing your moth – but he doesn't have time to finish his sentence because he is struck by his son's girlfriend's crying face and the fact that one side of her head looks as if someone has shorn a plant with little care. She looks like a small child who has been deliberately wounded. Suddenly, the father remembers again that he wanted to marry someone else when he was younger, a woman who lived nearby but his own mother at the time had said no, presenting instead this wife who he does love now and the father thinks that maybe this is what happens, we run circles around each other as a family, *young old young*, and here is his son in the middle of losing someone like he was once in the middle of losing someone and how they are both losing the mother *young old young.*

From the other room the mother calls and the girl leaves, still wailing. Without a word to each other the father and son present themselves to the dying woman and say, Everything is fine, You should go back to sleep.

The girl goes back home and falls into her mother's arms who says, What happened? but not before running her hand over the girl's head. This is the thing, the mother says, you gave him too much power, and the girl says, What power? And the mother who knows that the daughter will have to cobble together a dynamite personality one day to get through life successfully – remember if Mohammed cannot go to the mountain the mountain will come to Mohammed, the winner is always a man named Mohammed – but her poor baby, My poor baby, she says. She cradles her daughter's head in her lap and says softly, It will grow back, as if hearts are things that grow back and men are roots you can pull out of the ground and toss away.

The wig arrives at the house on a day when the father and the son are home and the mother is feeling better. The father brings in the box and puts it on the bed and carefully cuts the tape on the carton with a little razor blade, sets that aside and opens the box, pushes aside the crêpe paper. He moves the box onto the mother's lap. With a cry of delight the mother lifts up the wig with her bruised hands. It's beautiful, she says patting the hair, Oh, it really is beautiful. She begins to cry and tells the boy, You must call her and tell her she is beautiful. She takes off her scarf and fixes the wig on her head and by the doorway, her son leans against the door. For a second the only thing the room consists of is how happy his mother is.

Hair

When they bury her, they bury her with the wig. The girl does not come to the funeral, having transcended the relationship enough by then to be telling her friends I was dating a psychopath.

The boy even calls the girl and tells her about the funeral before it happens, but she hmms and haws having discovered some hardness in the story, some new asphalt to coast on. She is learning that she does not want to settle into adulthood with nothing to show for her youth except some pictures of herself in varying poses with hair at different lengths. Here it is long, here it is short, here it is gone and now it's back again. She is learning not to be kind for the sake of being kind and her mother is sad about this hardness that has arisen in her daughter, but you cannot unlearn a lesson, and her daughter is already practicing how to wield this lesson in the world.

The boy breathes a sigh of relief immediately after the funeral and wonders about all the paths to tragedy. For example, the hair was dead when it became a wig and for a while, in-between, when she got better for a week, his mother used to hang it up on the coatrack carefully at night and he would imagine that because it was dead hair, it would soon begin to fall, strand by strand onto the floor.

By now, the boy thinks after a month has passed, *it must be caked in mud so many feet deep in the ground, damp and splitting.* Or maybe if he and his father dug up the grave in a year's time there would be nothing there at all except the hair once given from a woman to a woman, still long, shining and straight, also some bones.

The girl's hair grows. She oils it with coconut oil nightly, sometimes uses yogurt and fenugreek. It grows down her back, and for her wedding three years later she has it up in a princess braid, pinned a thousand different ways so her husband has to spend the first two hours of their wedding night helping her take it out. It crackles hard with hairspray underneath her when they lie in bed together, too tired to touch. When they divorce three years later, she cuts it off, so it looks like a boy's, dyes it bright red so people say, This is what happens, in whispers behind her back. She travels soon after, the dye fading now in the short stumpy hair, feeling invisible and light.

The hair is just touching her shoulders when she meets someone again. It grows faster than it has ever grown when she is in love and happy, when she is pregnant with her first daughter.

The girl and her husband shave their daughter's head four days after the birth. Her husband holds the baby's head as if it is a bird, the blade sharp and keen across the soft malleable temple.

When the girl breastfeeds her daughter, her hair begins to turn white, as if the baby is leeching the color out, and soon it is falling in thick clumps and sticking to the shower drain. Pregnancy hair is short-lived, a friend – a mother three times over by then – tells her on the phone. The girl cuts it off again. Then it grows slowly. She lets it wisp onwards for years, through new jobs, illnesses, nights spent lying awake, her mother's death, and then begins to dye it black. She asks her daughter if she looks like Madonna, *young old young*, and the daughter (now a teen) says, Who is Madonna?

When the girl dies, it is this daughter who bathes her, who curls shampoo into the soft wrinkles set deep in her mother's still scalp. Hope is always a daughter with an unbroken heart. In the distance the line of mountains snakes on across the horizon and reaches singing for the women too.

You can do anything

Mahreen Sohail on Hair

Mahreen Sohail has published stories in The Kenyon Review, Guernica Magazine and The Pushcart Prize Anthology. 'Hair' first appeared in Granta magazine in April 2020, in the first UK Covid lockdown.

We spoke via video call between London and Islamabad in February 2021, in the third lockdown. In her discussion of the story, Mahreen spoke about the parts of the story which needed meticulous control, and the parts where she was free to surprise herself.

What was your first inspiration for this story? What did you want to write about?

I was talking to a friend about how you know when a relationship is over, how you can like someone and then they seem suddenly irritating and even physically unattractive – I thought the idea would make for a funny story, a bit ironic.

When you developed it were you surprised where you took the story or was this planned?

No, I was surprised. Initially the story was about the girl and boy. Then suddenly it was about hair instead and I found that could be the engine that would give the story a richness and carry the momentum. I am a little bit obsessed with hair – for women around the world there is a lot attached to it.

A wealth of themes and ideas recur in the story. Was there a lot of conscious planning and redrafting to bring out these elements?

The first draft for me is always draft zero (a friend came up with this). It is like it doesn't exist. I write it out and I hope that no one will ever see it, I even look at it with half-closed eyes. Then later I go back and think *this is interesting, this is something I can develop.*

Going over it, I realised the plot of the story, which was essentially that of a guy chopping off a girl's hair, was pretty violent and there was room for these characters to be more nuanced. Secondly, there's cancer in this story – I've had a loved one suffer from cancer and I feel like being in that position of not exactly having cancer but being in close proximity to someone who does have it opens you up to second-hand sympathy that you can, if you want, take advantage of. Even though the boy in the story does something that's pretty bad, I thought there was space for him to attract the readers' sympathy a little bit and that made for an interesting situation too.

It became clear that the women were also attached to each other in some way, through their hair and how they relate to it – these nuances I had to put into the story later and tweak, but the plot came immediately.

So the dramatic irony of the girl feeling she has the boy for life when actually she has disgusted him, that was there in draft zero?

Yes. I knew when I was writing it that it was funny. I feel asymmetrical bobs can go either way – they're really in the eye of the beholder.

When the guy thinks *am I a psychopath?* that I had to think about; he could not just be a guy going around chopping off sleeping people's hair, he also had to have something going on besides that. I wanted him to be aware of his loss of control because his mother is dying. He's not essentially a bad person, he just doesn't know how to fix what's happening around him. Just let me fix this girl somehow, he thinks. With the boy in the story there's definitely a sense of a flailing about. It's a strange reaction to your mum's cancer to put a wig on her. He continues to flail throughout. I wanted people to have sympathy for him as well. It's like he wants the attention on himself

In the first half, men have the greater agency; it's only in the second half that the women take it back.

I felt in some places your writing appeared to become aware of itself, in sentences like: 'Feels herself rising to the middle of this story.' Why did you make this choice?

When I was writing this, the girl was kind of a doormat at the beginning. And this sentence was me at that moment reminding myself she should not be a doormat. There seemed no way to address it other than addressing it directly in that moment.

Sometimes I think that short stories should do this more. We seem to be really into smoke and mirrors and tricks and stuff but there's something really powerful about stating something as it is. That particular line is me saying what this story is about. It foreshadows that she will become the centre.

You use something similar when you write 'Reassembles her face so that it resembles a scissor,' and 'having discovered some hardness in the story.' What was your purpose here? Could they – the first one especially – be an intentional confounding of how prose can sink thoughtlessly into using techniques from cinema?

I have a lot of feelings about how women are told to be, the idea that, if you want to make it in the world, you have to be bossy and stronger than you are. Which I think there's a sadness to, which the girl's mother recognises.

Non-cinematic? Not consciously but I agree with that sentiment. There's a certain power you have as a writer where you can tell or just state something in a way that's ultra defamiliarised that you can't do so easily with other mediums without coming across as cringey.

You can have a plot and these moments of extreme honesty and the author inserting themselves into the text – these are the things that are super exciting about writing and literature, that you can have all of these different elements and if you put them together they still work.

I was thinking about Rick Moody's title story of his short story collection *Demonology*. It's about his sister passing away, although by the end of it he changes tack and includes himself which is like a punch to the gut. It's exciting for me, the possibility that you can, if you do it well, do anything.

How would you describe the voice you created for this story? How did you come to it?

The voice came from the first line. I knew I didn't want a first person or a named third person narrator. The choice not to name them was very conscious. It gave me this feeling of freedom as I was writing, as if I didn't know the characters either.

I read 'Light' by Lesley Nneka Arimah. In it there's one named character but otherwise no one is named, it's just the girl and her mother and characters described by their relationships. There's something freeing about that because it allows you to go in many different directions. The character isn't pinned down to a name. You can play around with the fact that the girl is just a girl until she becomes a woman, and it becomes a question to consider when that disconnect happens.

It's a subtle way of reinforcing how these characters are connected to each other; mother, mother-in-law.

You can do anything

The first line has no tricks or disorientation; it sets out the story. It's easy to write like that – the boy does this, the girl does that, the mother feels – the voice allows you to inhabit all of the characters equally. There's a widening that happens when you address them as 'the boy' or 'the girl.'

By being more distant from them, you give them more room to manoeuvre?

Exactly. For me, and I think the reader, there is more room for the characters to accommodate other possibilities – it makes their relationships to each other much stronger. It also places you at a distance from them; it's almost like you're looking down on them, watching this happen and that allows for an element of humour as well. This idea of us watching this show.

It gives us more windows.

How did you maintain the balance of the dying mother's story with the girl's story? What effects did you want to create with their juxtaposition?

It seems like the girl is the core of the story but it's actually the mother. It's her death that is at its centre, and what's going to happen with her. There was something beautiful about the two women being connected by hair – at different ends of their lives. Somehow it allows them to transcend this young man who's kind of beside the point. The juxtaposition of the two women, I thought, did a good job of making sure the boy was not the story.

Amy Hempel, who wrote 'In the Cemetery Where Al Jonson is Buried', says in *The Paris Review* that her stories come from two places (I'm paraphrasing). One is 'whatever I do, I have to tell you this,' and the other one is 'whatever I do, I can't tell you this.' This has stayed with me, these two ways from which a story comes. It starts for the boy with 'I can't tell you this' when he doesn't know how to talk about his situation, and then it becomes for the girl 'I have to tell you this' when she reclaims the story.

So you split those two impulses into different characters?

Not consciously but a lot of the time I'm writing I'm thinking about this issue because it's a very interesting tension. I think the mother is the person we are circling and she never comes to the surface of the story, although her impending death is at the core of it and the boy and the girl react to the mother's death in very different ways.

How did the plot develop? Did you let the characters surprise you or was this more rigorously planned?

In the ending, the girl surprised me, yes. This story ended at the funeral originally, although something about it didn't feel complete yet.

And the father also surprised me. There's a sadness to him, he's watching his wife die, uncertain if he loves her any more, him now reaching the end of his life too. I did not think the characters would go where they went. I felt I needed to include more about his life because I didn't want it to be just a man mourning his wife or a man who's just indifferent to his wife dying. It needed to be something in between.

It's not interesting for it to be either/or. What *is* interesting, especially when we're talking about love, is it's always more nebulous than it's presented – I wanted to capture that with all of the characters. The girl does that when she's making these conscious choices, for example, if she cuts off her hair her boyfriend will love her. It's not a psychologically sound choice. But she's making these transactional decisions because we think like that – if I do this maybe that will happen.

Why was the funeral not the correct ending for you?

The guy's story was still too much and the piece would have

ended with the man if it finished there. Afterwards, I actually wrote two or three pages more and then realised I had gone too far and had to trim. I thought I had to give this woman a fair shot to live and breathe on the page now the initial thing had ended.

The last page seems to accelerate and then broaden out, away from the immediate situation. Why did you choose this ending?

The widening of it came out of nowhere. And then I read it again and thought *oh yes, this is correct.* The voice is looking down and then suddenly you feel you know the characters, as if you are very close to them, like you've been through this thing with them, so it felt appropriate to really really zoom out and say what happened generationally, to have the women going on – there was a certain joy to that. The daughter watches her mother's hair turn white.

Those last pages really surprised me, I don't know where they came from. Rana Dasgupta, who edited the issue, sent me notes on the story, he wrote: 'I want you to realise you describe the woman's life as getting married, giving birth and dying – is that all you want her life to be?' He wanted to show me it was a conscious decision I was making. To be honest, I hadn't thought of it like that, and I went back and thought, well, for a lot of people that *is* their life but there must be a way to show it's broader than that as well.

So she has a daughter, illness, jobs, a range of things happening to her. I tweaked that a little bit to make it feel like it was bigger than her just getting married and dying. His note was really useful there. It's easy to fall into that trap when you're writing a life too. A lot of my stories are centred around women in marriages or circling marriages and I always have to remind myself to make a conscious decision to broaden that a little. Then I think to myself why am I broadening this if for a lot of women that is their life?

You said also you overshot with the ending in one draft and had to cut it back. Could you say why you chose against that other ending?

The point of me carrying on the story after the funeral was to have her reclaim the story but I was hammering the point too hard. I had to take it back and see if this could be said in fewer words. If something can be said in fewer words then I think that's always better. I cut out the funeral scene and a few other scenes between the girl and her friends which I had added to give her some dimension, thinking 'maybe she needs friends' but then I cut them out.

What did you learn in the writing of this story?

I'm trying to think of an answer that would be publishable and maybe that's different from the truthful answer. The truth is that I am trying to write now and I realise I have no idea what I am doing, so each time it's like starting from scratch. When I was writing 'Hair', I felt just like when writing is working, it's working. I only had to do about four or five drafts. I call it a type of gift story. There are stories that I work very hard at but this came quite naturally. The stakes were very low. I was in the middle of moving from Pakistan to the States and I was writing because, in the process of moving, I didn't want to lose touch with writing. I think this gave me a kind of freedom.

Theophrastus and
the Dancing Plague

by Jessie Greengrass

I t is the November of 1526 when Theophrastus Bombastus von Hoenheim, known as Paracelsus – wandering physician, alchemist, heretic and, on occasion, mercenary – comes to Strasbourg. His fame precedes him: stories that, in the main, aren't good, or aren't true. For himself he doesn't care what people say until he's drunk; but six drinks in and he'll rise up from his bench by a rotting bar at the end of another filthy alley and he'll point his fat finger at a stranger and say, *What do they call me?*, and although at first people will demur, he'll keep asking until someone obliges: *They call you a fraud, man. A charlatan. You couldn't cure the Lord himself.* There are other things they won't say out loud, not even drunk and in company and with all the lamps lit: that they heard he made a pact and now the devil walks beside him; that he could kill you without touching you, without seeing you. Without even knowing your name.

After he's goaded them to rudeness he'll shout and curse, and after that he'll drink with boorish determination until it's time to slide from the bench and crawl to his bed, which might be above the bar or might be in the gutter, depending. It's a mystery to Theophrastus why people don't like him. He'd be the first to admit that he's brutish at times and doesn't wash as often as he should and that he fails to meet questions with humility, taking all enquiries to be challenges – but somehow he doesn't make the connection. Only the sick don't mock him, but then half the time they don't pay him, either.

In a ditch two days from Strasbourg with nothing for company but a half-lame horse and the impassive, impersonal constancy of the rain, he celebrates his thirty-third birthday. He feels older although he doesn't look it; he looks like a baby grown to the size of a man, a monstrous sort of creature in a child's unlined skin. He's tired. And wet, too. And cold. He's been all over Europe, and he's been to Alexandria and to Turkey, and he's been deep into Africa where he was terrified by a crocodile which, he says, getting the timing of the joke just wrong, is not as funny as it sounds; and he says he's been to a place so far north that a day lasts a year and it's nothing but snow between you and black water, but he's told that story so often drunk that sober he can't remember if it's true. He used to think that all was mirror and if he knew the world he'd know man and knowing man he'd know God's mind and medicine; but lately the sight of a candle through a window makes him feel sad like he used to love someone but now he's forgotten their face. It's time to settle. In the town he pays his gold and joins a guild, and they write his name in the book, and he is a citizen.

The adjustment is not as easy as he might have hoped. He isn't used to so much sameness, so much order. Citizenship gives him a feeling of indemnity, but he's easily bored. As distraction, he becomes interested in the plagues of dancing to which Strasbourg is prone, and begins to collect details of the last one, eight years before: he thinks there might be something there, some source of illumination which, once seen, might afford him the greater comprehension he has so long been seeking. It is his belief that all things are connected, and in them an echo of God. This echo he strives to hear. He starts to ask around. Strasbourg is not the first place he's been to that has this kind of story. He's heard of cases from Utrecht to Augsburg to Zurich. In Erfurt he heard how one morning in spring all the children danced out in the direction of Arnstadt and only half of them came back, and in the Moselle valley they showed him the place where the weight of dancing made a bridge collapse, tipping its burden into the river below; and looking down to where the water fitted and shook, he felt a tug like fingers pulling on a thread looped round the bony place above his heart. In a town in Switzerland they told him how a novice at the monastery, possessed by a demon, danced himself to death in the abbey graveyard; although a woman with a canker the size of an onion on her thigh said bollocks, everyone knew the lad had gone over to the next valley to get wed and died twenty years back the father of nineteen children, ten of them living and only eight of those his wife's. The Strasbourg plague is different, though. It's more recent, and although a lot has changed in eight years you can still see the signs of it, down by the tanners' guild. Even given a regrettable tendency on the part of the common man to exaggeration and hyperbole, the delineation between fact and myth is mostly clear. He learns that it started in July, the latest summer in a long line of bad summers broken by worse winters, years in which rain was longed for and then, when it came, came too late, rotting in the sheds what little had been yielded by the earth. A woman, Frau Troffea, in the middle of some other task, put down what she was holding and walked out into the street and started to dance. She danced all day, jigs and roundels and odd, listing hops, and her arms stretched up as if she were trying to catch hold of something just beyond her reach, her husband trailing behind like discarded clothing. When she slept it was because exhaustion took her: she fell where she stood and they carried her home but in the morning she was gone again. By the end of a week you could see the fine bones of her ankle showing through the torn flesh like wire. There was a crowd round her. Most of them had come to jeer, or to preach or pray, but some had come to dance and found they couldn't stop. By the start of August there were nearly a hundred of them and more coming all the time. The town council, under advice from the doctors, had the tanners' guild emptied, and they had a stage built and they hired musicians and then they had the dancers herded in. The theory was, the dancing was a sort of fever and you had to break it: whip the dancers up and spur them on and if they looked like flagging beat them until the crisis came, but the crisis didn't come. The physicians kept on with it anyway, because it ought to work, even if it didn't. Theophrastus thinks this is what's wrong with doctors, by and large. Sometimes, when he looks for God, he looks at the world and all he sees is decay. By his accounting, to extract one ounce of original substance takes twenty pounds of matter and the rest just salt and vapour, ash; and although there'll come a time a few years off when he'll find it oddly comforting to be able to look at himself and think that he contains at least a grain of good, now he sees only the balance of impurity.

Every day through the August of 1518 more of the afflicted were led into the guild, and at night the families came and searched in the corners where the dead lay kicked aside by those still up on what was left of their feet. The way Theophrastus hears it, Strasbourg felt like hell, that month, with the heat of summer on the city and the nights so short they seemed little more than the guttering of the day's thin, sharp, shadowing light, and over all the insidious, inescapable whine of the music. One man, after a few drinks, tells Theophrastus that he felt it himself: the pull of it, the promise, the way it seemed you could leave the grinding and step outside and be lifted up, be raised high, and you'd never have to think of anything again: not the price of bread nor the plague spreading down from the north nor whether Luther was right about your soul. The man says it was

like God speaking, telling you to follow; and then he covers his
mouth and looks around, in case anyone heard the blasphemy.
Theophrastus watches him and wonders if this man was one
of the ones who had listened. What he's noticed is, there are
plenty who survived but he's only ever met the ones who say it
happened to a friend. Personally, he wouldn't be one to blame. In
his opinion they were guilty of nothing more than the weakness
of will that allowed their reason to be overpowered by their
imagination. He thinks, it's the first one with whom the blame
lies: Frau Troffea, who was surely lazy and vindictive. She did
it out of spite, he thinks, to avoid the work her husband gave
her; and then the others, poor impoverished souls, followed.
Theophrastus doesn't like women. They unnerve him, and also
he can't see the point of them: you can't train them and if you
beat them they sulk. He himself avoids them. Certainly he has
not even an ounce of forgiveness to spare for this one; or perhaps
it is not so much that he won't forgive as that he is neither
close enough nor far enough away to see her situation with the
compassion it would take to let her actions pass. After all, he
has seen what she must have seen: the dead and the starved,
the rotten, the lost, the apostate priests damning the souls of
their congregations, the dissenters in town squares holding their
guts like gifts – and it would not occur to him to allow this
as explanation, still less excuse. On the other hand, although
he might be mocked, he is neither castigated nor reviled, not
yet; and he is not an empathic man, lacking the capacity to
understand except through experience. To imagine the lives of
others would demand perhaps too deep a plumbing of himself.

For all he thinks he's found a home there, Strasbourg doesn't
last. His opinions are too forth-right, his manner unrepentant,
and he won't concede, even when it's obvious that he's wrong.
It's a problem with his work, this: since he cannot admit to
having made a mistake he must incorporate everything he has
ever thought, everything he has ever asserted to be the case, into

his taxonomy, and now even he can't remember the meanings of all the words he's needed to invent. He is challenged to a public disputation and inevitably, because he stutters and splutters and swears and is a terrible public speaker, and also because the town's population already regards him with derision bordering on contempt, he loses. He's considering a number of responses, each of them worse than the last, when he's called away to treat the infected leg of the publisher Johann Froben, and it seems best not to return. He goes instead to Basle where he is given a job at the university, but his appointment is by the town council against the wishes of the medical faculty, and is not a success. Theophrastus gives a public lecture, arriving on stage before Basle's civic dignitaries with a bowl covered in a cloth; when he removes the cloth it is to display a fresh and well-formed human shit. Things deteriorate. Froben dies. A warrant is drawn up for Theophrastus's arrest. This becomes a pattern. In Alsace he sets up a laboratory but the authorities, forewarned, will not grant him residency. In an Esslingen basement he makes himself sick with chemicals and argues with his landlord; in Nuremburg his book on syphilis is banned and he publishes it anyway. He cannot resist the urge to blame, to rant and to polemicise. In St Gallen, a second patient dies – he writes: 'I do not know where I shall have to wander now; I do not care either, so long as I have helped the sick.' At Innsbruck, they do not even let him through the gates.

He stands outside the city wall and his hands, gripped in front of him, are draped in slack skin; his clothes are rags. It has not been easy to get here: he had to climb half a mountain; he was almost lost crossing the pass; he had to beg for food; a bandit tried to steal his money and, when it became clear that he had none, stole his hat. He can't even find it in himself to curse. It used to be that, in the space between sleeping and waking when sometimes one can hear music, Theophrastus would see it all and understand: what a man is, and how a body is constituted, how a life could be built from matter; and though in the morning he would have forgotten it all except the fact that he had known it, and though this would make him bad-tempered, giving him a permanent, irritating feeling that he'd misplaced something important, still it gave him the certainty that there was an answer. Now, those hypnagogic understandings seem no better than a joke. Where he used to see in God a guarantee of the universe's fundamental rationality, now he sees only a monstrous whimsy, and his desolation is so great that he feels his head might split across the crown from the pressure of it – and if, at this moment, he looks back to Strasbourg; if he looks back to Frau Troffea, whose despair or defiance of despair he had called spite, might he not feel something more like recognition, something like a stirring, or perhaps like being pierced. Might he not see how after years of shuffling to misery's stolid ostinato one's life might, in the space between this breath and the next, become intolerable; how, desperate for escape, one might step out into the street and, in the lifting of the breeze, find a call to more rapid movement; how fierce joy might rise in equal parts with anger and despair to fill and feed itself; and how, having started, one could not stop, there being no way out but to return.

Denied entry to Innsbruck, Theophrastus is at a loss. He can't stay where he is and, although he has nowhere to go, he is left no choice but to continue. Wearily he turns around, and begins the long walk back, towards the pass.

Story as a sort of argument

Jessie Greengrass on Theophrastus and the Dancing Plague

This story comes from the collection An Account of the Decline of the Great Auk, According to One Who Saw It, *for which Jessie Greengrass won a Somerset Maugham Award as well as the 2016 Edgehill Short Story Prize.*

Fittingly for someone with a background in philosophy, Jessie's discussion of the story explored the principles that underpin her writing. In her use of argument as a model for story-telling, she explained how writing towards an emotional 'conclusion' helped her understand what to cut out.

What was the initial inspiration for the story?

Initially I was interested in the dancing plagues. I was trying to find a way of writing about that topic – I read a lot about that but I couldn't find an 'in' to it, aside from writing a history of it or *making up* a protagonist which would have felt awkward.

I couldn't find a way of writing about it that wasn't a bit shambolic until I came across a mention of Paracelsus who wrote about the Strasbourg dancing plague. I knew a little about him and felt this would allow me to get into the subject without doing an enormous amount of explanatory work or historical invention.

What did you want the story to be? Where did you want to take this story?

Normally I have quite a clear idea – there would be a really specific thing, usually an image or feeling or circumstance that I want to write about.

With this story I think it was more just that it felt so resonant; the feeling that everyone had such a desperation, that there was no way to escape circumstances, which I guess has become weirdly more relevant lately.

These people were absolutely at the mercy of landowners, priests and the plague and there was nothing they could do about it, so I was fascinated by the idea that they might do something that seemed extremely odd and keep on doing it despite the fact that it became very evidently a bad idea, just because the alternative was going home.

I was also interested in the character of Paracelsus; he was a wandering mystic who kept trying to find a home across the European medieval landscape and every time it went wrong. I liked the idea that he was grasping at a way of making sense of the plague, that if he could understand what had made people do this then he could understand everything. He understood the world as a mirror of God – if you can understand what's happening here you can somehow use that to get divine leverage. It was this quest of understanding that I was trying to get at.

The thing about the dancing plague is it still elicits the same response; one still feels absolutely mystified by it. There is so much writing that tries to understand what happened and why it happened – was it mass hysteria or ergot poisoning? There are so many theories.

In the opening and elsewhere (when Theophrastus thinks that he contains 'a grain of good') you use some very long and involved sentences. Why do you alternate your quite clipped, restrained sentences with these longer, deeper ones?

I think of the story as a sort of argument; you set out your premises and then you reach a point where you draw the conclusion – the conclusion in a story is for me the reader's emotional response.

I think the contrast you're talking about is really important partly because I think it has more of an effect than if you're reading pages and pages of 'everybody was sad' which would make it begin to wash over you a little and lose its power. Whereas, if you have that contrast in the sentences then it allows you to notice the emotion more.

But also, just from a readability point of view, if you're writing stories – unless you're really really determined – you do have to try and use a variety of sentences to make a story readable or to some extent enjoyable.

I wondered if the two types of register mirrored Theophrastus' need for comprehensive understanding as he fights the emotional turmoil within him, as if maybe the contrast in the story is the same contrast within him?

This is probably the sort of thing that I don't tend to think about. I don't put a lot of thought into *why* the story needs to be as it is. I find the voice and *feel* that it works – it's like being able to just hear that a piece of music is in tune as opposed to having to think about it consciously.

Is that a skill that you've worked on and improved or is it an instinct you've always had?

It's something I've definitely got more confident with, but I think like all writing it's just something you get from reading a lot. The more you read the more you get an ear for what works or what you like and what's effective. I think that is primary. Then you can use that sense of what good writing is to try and do some.

It feels Theophrastus is the frame through whom we understand the dancing plague, yet they don't fully meet in the same story. How did you balance the different needs of these two aspects?

Originally, I wrote a lot more than there was in the finished story. Having Theophrastus as an inroad into it allowed me to cut out everything that wasn't relevant. Having him as a focal point did narrow things down and put constraints on the amount I could write about.

But that was only part of the point of it, the dancing plague was a fascinating idea but in order to make a story out of it you have to find a way to know what to leave out. This is particularly true when you're writing about anything historical. You have to find a way to get rid of the things that are really interesting but don't belong in the story.

To start with I thought the Theophrastus element was key but then as I edited it there were more and more bits where I thought: *that's really interesting and I really like it but it's not doing any work and it has to go.* If it's a cog turning by itself you have to cut it out of a short story.

And what about Theophrastus' own story and his emotional journey? Was that easy to fit in with the dancing plague?

The dancing plague came first. When I was looking at Paracelsus' life it was to find the bits that were relevant or interesting so the bits before and after this journey to Strasbourg, his attempt and failure to live there, all of this, if there's too much detail there you lose the point of the story so it has to be all cut out instead.

So the story of Paracelsus' disillusionment was a true story?

Yes, that's his life so far as it is possible to tell – he wrote many diaries and notebooks trying to produce a taxonomy of the entire world. It got so complicated he had to invent a language to deal with it all but he would end up forgetting what his invented language meant.

Paracelsus became a mythical figure – he was a real person but he was known afterwards as someone who had done a deal with the devil. I was interested in finding the root of what would make a man like that and a conclusion I came to is he would have to be quite unhappy but also driven, someone who knew he was looking for something, though he wasn't able to understand what it was.

I wondered if the Enlightenment was a fitting context to explore people's need to try and comprehend and impose order on the chaos. In this way was the story metaphorical?

I don't think it is specifically metaphorical. I think all writing is about itself and lots of other things. I was definitely trying to write about feelings that are familiar, so I would hope that some of it does feel resonant.

Your language very often has a factual, formal distance, when do you decide to shift into more metaphorical language such as 'guts like gifts'?

I don't think it's a decision – a lot of the early writing of anything is finding the voice to write it in. When I've got that, it becomes clear then how that voice would go; as I write it becomes more of a feeling than a conscious decision. I don't think things through very well before I do it. I write by writing.

So when you write you stick by what feels right for the voice and the story, but when you edit what do you do with this original draft?

I would have written loads, three or four times as much as

the finished story. I keep everything.

When I'm writing a novel, that work tends to happen at the beginning, the work of finding a voice, and I write four or five times what I need for the first chapter because what I'm trying to do is generate a voice. Once that's happened, it tends to go along more easily.

But with a short story, there isn't the space to generate the voice and so I tend to write a lot and cut and cut and cut it until I find the bits that work or the bits that I feel work.

What are the criteria for what works and what has to be cut?

First of all, bad stuff, which sounds like it's a really stupid thing to say but I mean I think it's important to acknowledge that a lot of the really early bit of any writing project is just awful, just excruciating – I will put in my will that someone will need to delete my hard drive because I can't bear the idea of someone reading that stuff.

Then, when all of that is gone, it becomes a case of weighing up what work everything does in the story. For example, I would ask: 'does this add to the point?' If it doesn't add then it doesn't really matter how good it is, it doesn't have a place.

That's when I get to the point of thinking about a piece that *I'm really happy with this but I can't put it in the story*, so I'll put it in a folder somewhere, and probably never use it because what am I going to do with offcuts of a story about Paracelsus and the dancing plague?

We see that Theophrastus is unpopular and controversial but I feel you didn't want to fully explain the medical and theological context. Did you make a conscious decision not to give a lot of context?

It was semi-conscious – there wasn't room for it unless what I'm doing is writing a semi-fictional slightly overwrought biography of Paracelsus, then that information didn't have a place in the story. It is possible that it is not a successful story – I don't know if I wrote it now, I would make the same decisions or maybe there was just not enough of a story there.

When you re-read it now, what do you think?

I think the writing is ok though I do think there is possibly a problem that the story is slightly tenuous, but I don't regret writing it. I wrote it eight or nine years ago and I would have hoped I had got better at writing just by dint of practice.

So it's not only reading but also practice that makes a good writer?

Yes, I think that reading is the starting point, and like any craft or any job, writing is a job – I like to think of it like a job or else you're in danger of becoming an awful example of humanity. It's a job, it's what I get paid to do so I must treat it like a job. And like any job, the hope is that you get better as you go along.

I think it was definitely a story that came out of my own interests – I don't think that's a bad thing and instead of thinking: *God, this would make a brilliant short story*, I thought: *this is really interesting and I want to write about it*, which is not a bad starting place I think.

You finish with 'Wearily he turns around and begins the long walk back, towards the pass.' Why did you want to end the story here? What did you want this ending to do?

Almost always I know what the ending is going to be before I know anything else. For example when I wrote *Sight* [published by JM Originals], I wrote the last sentence before I wrote anything else.

There are two ways I think about a story ending.

The first is a memory I have of someone telling me about a really bad ballet he'd gone to; all the dancers were quite bad although at the end of every movement they would just flick their fingers to try and look like the whole thing had been incredibly good. That really stuck with me. I think you can't just put a good flick on the end, you have to build a solid foundation for your ending.

This is particularly true with short stories. What I try to do in a story is create a thought – the ending is what the thought is driving towards. There's not much room in a short story to go off over here and there – you've only got space for one thought, and it has to do quite a lot of work.

The second thought about endings comes from Larkin's poems. He has incredible last lines which the whole poem is gearing up for. It's like opening doors. You can see the space beyond it and that's the poem. It's that space outside so I think it's always looking for that point at which I feel there's something beyond and what the story's done is opened itself onto that space. If you keep writing beyond that, you shut it down again – you have to leave it unexplored as that is the job of the imagination to some extent.

How well do you think your ending does that?

He walks up a hill. He surveys everything and then he turns and walks down again. I think that's the moment of 'I see it, I turn, I walk away into the rain.' That is the extra gesture. I would hope that the story before it does enough of the heavy lifting that there is a point to that.

What did you learn in the writing of this story?

About medieval philosophy?

Anything to do with writer's craft?

Nothing specific but I think it's all practice. I stopped writing short stories when I had children because I find I can write a novel in 45 minutes a day – I know where I left off and I can sit down and write for 45 minutes and stop. Then I have to look after the children which is my main job.

I can't write short stories like that because I have to have a period of time in which I can sit and actually write them. I can't just do a little bit and then leave it. It meant I didn't write any short stories at all for four or five years.

I've written some more recently, and I feel like writing short stories helped with writing novels. I very much think of writing novels as being like writing a series of short stories. I think of it sectionally – each section has to function in the way a short story does.

Conversely, the confidence that comes from writing novels has made it much easier as I've gone back to writing short stories.

Why does it take more than 45 minutes to write a short story?

A short story is a single entity, a single thought. I find it hard to write it by breaking it down, so I feel I need a few hours to write if not weeks and weeks.

Since my eldest child was born, I have written early in the mornings, starting work at 7 and stopping when my partner goes to work. That's the amount of time that I have, and I felt I couldn't keep a short story in my mind enough – it was too bitty. Although I think I might be able to do it now because I've had six years practice writing in really short spaces of time.

So you hold a short story more palpably in your head then?

There's just more space in a novel, so you can meander this way and that and can bring it back again. Whereas with a short story you can't just write yourself back around. You don't have the space – you have to go in a straight line.

Filamo

by Irenosen Okojie

The last monk told the tongue that holding a naked sheep's head underwater would undo it all. Some time before that, prior to the madness beginning, old Barking Abbey loomed in the chasm; grey, weather worn, remote. Inside the Abbey, a tongue sat in the golden snuff box on an empty long dining table; pink, scarred and curled into a ruffled, silken square of night. The previous week, the tongue had been used as a bookmark in a marked, leather bound King James Bible, page 45 where the silhouette of a girl had been cut out; loaded with words like *high, hog, clitoris, iodine, cake*, its moist tip glistening in temporary confinement. The week before that, the tongue had been left in the fountain at the back of the Abbey, between winking coins. There, it pressed its tip to a stray ripple, cold and malleable, shaping it into a weight, pulling it down, under, up again. Several weeks back, it had been in a hallway window, leaning into Mary's hands, whose fingertips tasted of a charred, foreign footprint from the grass. Her fingertips had sensed a change in the air before the monks came, when the corridors were quiet, expectant. Molecules had shifted in preparation for a delivery. The monks arrived through a hole in time on a cold, misty morning, transported via a warp in space that mangled the frequencies of past and present. They arrived curling hands that did not belong to them. Unaware that this would have consequences none foresaw, except a tongue bending in the background, unaware of the repercussions of time travel.

Each time the tongue was moved, it lost a sentence. The monks missed this in their ritual of silence. They had done for weeks; walking around rooms with arms behind their backs, bodies shrouded in heavy brown robes, shaven, sunken heads soft to the touch. They trod this new ground carrying yolks in their mouths, hardening as morning became noon, noon became evening, and evening became night.

One morning, the monks found a miller's wife gutted on the stone wall enclosing the allotment, a white felt cap shoved into her mouth, her husband's initials embroidered in blue at the top right corner of her bloody apron: V.O. They threw salt on her skin. The tongue tasted the sharpness, and that night, Dom Vitelli made the noise of a kettle boiling in his sleep. He began to tremble covered in a cold sweat. He fell to the floor, stuck.

The next morning, the monks rose to discover the empty well near the stone outbuilding surrounded by plump, purple jabuticaba fruit, tender and bruised, the colour dwindling in areas as though a god was sucking it through a crack in the sky. Lonely figures in their heavy brown robes the monks held their hands out as they circled the abbey. They heard the sounds of buses on the high street, car doors slammed shut, trains grinding to a halt. They caught items that fell through noise, things they had never seen; a white adapter plug from the sound of a plane speeding through the sky, a black dog muzzle Dom Oman later took to wearing when sitting by the fountain, a knuckle duster that fell from the sound of a baby crying. They placed these items at the altar in the chapel, flanked by candles on either side whose blue flames bent, then shrank sporadically. They took turns holding their palms over the flames. By the time the monks began their chores, the cockerel that had fallen over the walls from a car horn began to smash its beak into a jabuticaba fruit. Afterwards, it jumped into the stream connected to the Roding River, following a thinning, yellow light it attempted to chase into the next day.

The tongue was warm in Filamo's pocket, pressed against a copper coin bearing the number two in Roman lettering. The musty taste of old items passing through lingered. Filamo, a cloaked figure, a betrayer amongst the monks, stood outside the prayer room, fingering a swelling on the tongue, listening quietly. Dom Emmanuel paced inside, the only other place speaking was permitted aside from supper during this imposed period of silence. A slightly forlorn figure, he shook. The bald patch on his head looked soft like a newborn's. Light streamed through the stained glass window where three naked cherubs wore angry, adult expressions and had changed positions again overnight. One lay on its side holding an ear, the other was eating stigmata injuries and the third at the bottom-left corner had tears running down its cheeks into the jabuticaba fruit growing through its chest. Dom Emmanuel faced the silence of the cross on the nave wall without the figure of Christ, which had turned up at supper two days before, bleeding between slices of bread. There were three deep, wooden pews behind the Dom, half-heartedly built, scratched on the seating. Dom Emmanuel began to walk back and forth. Then, he paused momentarily as though to catch his breath, chest rising and falling. He held his arms out, confessing that lately he had begun to worry about his lover withering in a wormhole. The man Dom Emmanuel loved had not made it through this time, stuck in a winter that would quickly ice his organs and distribute the seven languages he spoke into the orbit for other monks to grab and stow away along with new disguises.

Dom Emmanuel could feel that cold in his bones, an absence of language, lightness in his tongue. Recently, Dom Emmanuel had dreamt of them running through lush, sunlit fields naked, penises limp at first, then turgid, moist at the tips, till thick spurts of sperm dribbled and their irises glinted. He missed the warmth of holding another body skin to skin, the innocence of early youth, the freedom of making mistakes. He moaned that his hands ached; that they had begun to talk to him, consumed by restlessness, till he sat up in bed sweating, tense, listening to a distant mangled cry travelling towards his organs, to his hands. For days the cry had come to him each night while the others slept, on each occasion, magnified by the constant silence, taut, suffocating. The cry grew in volume, weight, intent. Till he was led by it, until he found himself stumbling outside into the grounds, disrobing by the darkened stream gleaming in the night. Naked, covered in bite marks, he hunched down to catch things from the water; Siamese green lizards who shared an Adam's apple, a piece of jabuticaba fruit which grew another layer of purple skin each time you touched it, one cherub whose eyes had blackened from things it had witnessed upstream, a lung wrapped in cling film. Surrounded by his discontented small audience, Dom Emmanuel removed the cling film, crying as he ate flesh. It tasted like a man he once paid four gold coins in Tenochtitlan to keep him company, to be rough then tender with him afterwards, who had stuck his curious tongue into his armpits as if digging for his body's secrets using a pliable instrument. Dom Emmanuel did not turn around when Filamo moved towards him lifting the blade. The cut to his neck was swift. He fell to the floor, blood gushing. The cry from his lips was familiar. It had been chasing him for days. He pressed his hands desperately against his neck, attempting to catch one last item rising through the blood. Dom Emmanuel died thinking of his lover's sour mouth, praying into it. The wound on his neck a cruel smile, clutching the lines of an old rectory sign bearing Roman number two in the left corner, his talking, gnarled hands slowly eroding. And half his body purple from a winter he already knew. While the monks scattered in shock, the tongue inherited Dom Emmanuel's last words, *El Alamein.*

When the saints arrived through their time canon, continuing their ancient tradition as watchmen over the monks, the night was onyx-shaped. A faint howl followed them onto the tower. The Abbey was formidable in the moonlight; imposing, damp, grey, surrounded by high stone walls. The saints were orange skinned from the Festival of Memory. Each had a feature missing but something to replace it within their bodies. Saint Peter was missing an ear, yet had a small, translucent dragon's wing growing against a rib. Saint Augustine had lost a finger on his left hand but had two hearts; one pumping blood, the other mercury, so much so his tongue became silvery at particular angles. Saint Christopher had lost an eye and gained a filmy, yellow fish iris that cried seawater no matter his mood. This time, each had been fired from a canon. Temporarily deaf, they clutched instructions for short transformations in golden envelopes. They wandered the cold halls lined with carvings and paintings on the walls, while the monks were gathered at supper, oblivious.

The saints deposited the envelopes beneath their beds. Each individual instruction for transformation sealed, yet written in the same long, right leaning handwriting by the same white feather dipped in blue ink. Each slip of yellow paper wrinkled at the corners, worn from weather, prayer, silence. Then, the saints fashioned three flagpoles from sticks they found in the cellar. They planted them on the grounds. The blue flag for go, red for pause, breathe, green for transform. Afterwards, on their journey back to two golden towers erected between wormholes, the saints became infants in the wind.

Later that night, the remaining Doms filed from the front of the abbey holding their golden envelopes. Dom Ruiz led the way, stopping to take his position at the green flagpole. The other Doms followed. Dom Mendel, slighter than the rest took a breath on the steps by the Roding's stream. The white hexagon several feet from the flagpoles spun seductively. In the library window, old leather bound books nursed the wisdom of hands

slowly erased by time. The Doms took their positions on all
fours. Light trickles of dark rain began to fall. They uttered
Pater tollis peccata. Their mouths distorted. The bell rang. They
darted forward, towards the centre and each other growling. A
sharp, splintered pain shot through their heads. Spots of white
appeared in their vision. Bones cracked as they expanded, organs
grew, teeth lengthened, fur sprouted, hooves appeared, nostrils
widened. Their sense of smell heightened. Dom Ruiz became a
boar lunging at Dom Mendel the centaur, chasing him with an
urgency that had his teeth chattering. Dom Kamil became an
epicyon hunting Dom Augustine the procoptodon between all
three flagpoles, through the other side of the white hexagon
where the static hissed, then back up again. They snarled at
the skyline, leaping, rushing; following the strong scent of old
flesh emanating from the soil. They buried their faces in it,
dug leaving large prints around the abbey that had a peculiar
beauty from above. Three hours later, they retreated back to
their starting positions becoming men again, exhausted bodies
heaving. Speckles of blood fell on the golden envelopes, over the
lines in foreign hands that had arranged into blueprints.

There were always injuries during a transformation. But the
small, morphing nucleuses they had generated would flatten
in their brains, rising again when necessary, mimicking the
silhouettes of tiny watchmen. As their breathing steadied, they
studied the red flag flapping in the wind for stop.

After the transformation, the silence within the abbey was
heavier, loaded. Having been banished by the saints for the
fallen monk in their midst, each monk was busy dealing with
the repercussions of their borrowed hands. And who knew what
that could do to a man? Seeds of doubt and mistrust had begun
to take root in this fertile ground of the unspoken, watered by
the saliva of sealed envelopes. The monks did not venture beyond
the abbey, afraid of being sucked into a vacuum of noise they
would not recognise. Noises of a future they felt unprepared

for, frightened that the influences of an outside world would somehow shorten their time at the abbey. Everything they needed was within the abbey's walls. They grew their own food using the allotment out back. At least 12 chickens were enough to feed from for a while, producing eggs for breakfast and the occasional comic attempt at escape. One chicken laid ten eggs that would not hatch, each filled with a finger of a new monk poking through deep red yolks. Somehow the Jesus figurine had found its way to these eggs. Stained by mud, it sat amongst them as they rolled and the other chickens leapt over the sound. Fed on bits of sullied bread, little Jesus waited patiently for a different kind of resurrection.

The saints made several visits back to the abbey through their time canon to deliver items; salt, a bow and arrow, a television remote, nails, a hammer, three serrated knives. Several days after the transformation, Dom Augustine woke in the middle of the night barking like a dog, tongue slightly distended, skin clammy. The next morning, he began to set animal traps around the grounds; one on top of the tower, one in the allotment, one behind the middle pew in the prayer room, under his bed, one on the white hexagon slowly fading from damp and cold. After all, who knew what a man's shadow would do while he pretended to look the other way? Dom Augustine felt a panic rising inside him. Each day his tongue loosened further, as if it would fall out at any moment. He did not know whether it was his increasingly intensified barking at nights that was the cause or his particular kink from banishment, from flight. There were always complications. He had arrived in the main chapel, between two tall marble grey pillars, deposited on the alabaster altar, naked and wrapped in a thin silvery film reflecting past angles of light. His limbs had hurt, his head throbbed. His breaths were slow, deep, attempting to acclimatise. He had broken through the film, instinctively grabbing at items from a past that would never appear, knocking over two large, white candlesticks on either side. Famished, he scrambled along the cold altar. He looked down; his gaze met the knowing blue eyes of a cherub who jumped up and down excitedly, showing him its scarred back from repeatedly falling through stained glass windows. Its mouth was purple after eating a combination of plump fruits and unidentifiable things. He'd broken his hands in just like all the other Doms; carving a small Jesus figurine, fixing the hole in the cellar roof, building a pantry. The ache in his hands never fully left, only dulling with time. His fear of items and sounds from the outside threatening to infiltrate the abbey had become so potent, one afternoon he had been washing his hands in holy water by the pantry when the sound of an axe lifting, falling, chopping, breaking, smashing had almost deafened him. Slow at first, coming from afar. Then closer, louder, heavier till he curled up by the metallic bowl of water screaming then barking, breaking the silence.

A week after Dom Augustine set the animal traps, parts of his body were found in each one. Pieces in the traps by the fading white hexagon looked like an offering. The axe the saints delivered had vanished. The tongue in Filamo's pocket dined on splattered blood.

It was a chilly evening on the occasion Dom Kamil decided to perform his act of rebellion against the silence. A light frost covered the grounds, more jabuticaba fruit from the well scattered. Large pillars at the abbey's entrance bore tiny cracks oozing a sticky, thin sap. The intricate, golden chapel ceiling depicting Old Testament scenes began to shed tiny specks of gold from the corners. Only an observant eye would notice the figures had began to head in the opposite direction. Metallic bowls of holy water carefully placed outside room entrances collected reflections as if they were a currency. Dom Kamil awoke to find himself doused in kerosene and Doms Ruiz and Mendel absent. Throat dry, he trembled before swinging his legs over the bed onto the floor. The smell of kerosene was acrid. He did not call out. Instead, he slipped his dull, weighty brown cloak on, briefly running a hand over the length of wooden flute he'd kept close during the daytimes. For weeks he had found the silence unbearable, craving the joy music brought. He had resorted to wandering around the abbey with the flute he'd made secretly, rubbing his hands along it when his fingers curled and flexed with intent. Beyond the abbey walls, an ambulance siren wailed. Dom Kamil rushed outside, at least 50 yellow notes were strewn on the frosted ground. He scrambled between each one, eagerly opening them but they were mockingly empty. Distraught, he pulled the flute from his pocket and began to play. When Filamo set him alight he did not stop, playing urgently until he fell to his knees, the heat of the flames licking his skin, veins, blinding him. The sound of the flute hitting cold ground reverberated in the abyss, the ambulance siren shattered. A dark curl of smoke shrunk into the tongue poking out from Filamo's pocket contemptuously.

The next morning, the two remaining Doms wandered the halls with the taste of kerosene in their mouths.

On the fated Sunday that followed, Dom Ruiz and Dom Mendel began their last set of chores for the week orchestrated by the saints, setting scenes for destruction; ripping the pages of books in the library, defacing the expressions of religious figures in paintings hanging on walls, smashing up the organ in the chapel nobody had been allowed to play, flinging the black and white keys over the bodies of ten monks in the deep, open grave tucked behind the stone steps. They sprinkled salt on those bodies. And when those monks' mouths were sealed shut again by snow from a future winter, they fed the chickens communion. After dying the underside of their tongues purple, they fished out the animal traps, assembling them into a circle at the abbey's entrance because their hands could not help themselves. They danced within the circle until sweat ran down their backs, till their legs ached and the skyline became a blur.

The nuclei embedded in their brains rose, bubbled, spat. They danced for what felt like an eternity until finally they crawled indoors. Heavy eyed and wary of collapsing in their sleeping quarters, they sat across from each other at the long dining table, watching, waiting. They dared not sleep, until the saint in their peripheral vision began to scream, burning bright, burnished orange smog into their heads.

Dawn arrived to discover Dom Ruiz slung over the bell, hands clinging limply to a thick, white rope, face battered beyond recognition. He dangled like a grisly gift a god had despatched. Meanwhile the tongue ran its moist tip along the bruises on Filamo's hands.

Spat out from another chasm, Dom Mendel lay sprawled on a wide patch of the Abbey's green surrounded by concrete paths. Time travel flight had occurred again. He knew it from the trembling in his knees, the ache spreading in his chest, the blockage in his ears slowly thinning, popping. His bruised hands were numb, stiff after being curled in the same position for hours. As though he'd been inserted into a corner of sky trying to balance, fingers instinctively wrapping around the shadows of lost items. Every junction fell off the map each time. A severed organ floating in white smoke till it disappeared. He sat up gingerly, taking small gulps of air. It felt like spring. Bright sunlight shrouded everything. The abbey was a carcass of its former self, its high walls reduced to mere remains. The sound of cars on the roads around it was jarring, alien. Mouth dry, barefoot, he stood slowly, noting the curfew tower in the distance. Exits at either end of the gutted, green gladiator-like pit beckoned. He decided to take the exit in front rather than the one behind him. He crossed some stone steps before landing in the graveyard. St Margaret's church stood to his right behind the tower a short walk away, bearing a flimsy white banner that said Café Open. People passed him throwing curious looks. Their clothing appeared odd and unfamiliar. He ran his hands over a few gravestones. The rough stone was cold to the touch. He grabbed sprigs of grass lining the bases, placed them on his tongue. Chewing, he made his way over the zebra crossing and onto the tail end of the market on East Street, drawn by the buzz of stalls, the cacophony of voices, the smell of meat hissing and spitting over a barbecue. He ran a finger over the tongue in his pocket as he heard the words *Bell End, Mango, fireworks, truncheon*. It curled against his finger as though acknowledging receipt. He walked along the market in shock, throngs of bodies spilling, multiplying and scurrying in every direction. On the high street, a man held a snarling Alsatian back from him. He could smell what it had eaten hours ago, a rotten, pungent scent. He resisted the urge to bare his teeth. Something lodged in his chest. His blood warmed. His heart began to mutate into the shape of the snarling dog's mouth, knocking against chest walls. He stumbled away from them. Trapped light in his retina split into tiny grains. Everything felt intense, gauzy. A bearded man bumped into him. He entered the sliding red door of the shopping centre almost by accident. Things bled into each other; the mannequins' mouths pressed against their glass confines, stitches from their hands coming undone, grazing his retina. Along the way his footsteps were dogged by sightings of familiar faces; Dom Emmanuel appeared on the raised stage for a concert, holding the knife that had killed him, slicing his neck repeatedly at the microphone. Dom Augustine's head lay in the Asda supermarket freezer, one animal trap snapping over his lost limbs as they reappeared. Dom Kamil sat engulfed in flames in a barber's chair. Dom Ruiz lay slumped over a Thomas the Tank Engine train, clutching one yellow note.

Dom Mendel passed a line of monks on an escalator, touching their shoulders but each one vanished. He was consumed by a loneliness so vast it was unknowable in this lifetime. He followed the exit out and back onto the streets. He kept walking, filled with a slow hypnotic wonder, wiping the dew off a car side mirror, becoming a small figure in its contained distances. Then on all fours, he scavenged in the bins outside the Yaki Noodle bar opposite the station. Afterwards, he walked around back streets staring at houses. He walked to Creekmouth, passing the mural of two men vomiting water, coddling ships while the land flooded. He studied the parked HGVs on industrial roads wondering what they contained, noticing the small factories and recycling stations. A veil of bleakness cloaked it all. The ghosts of Creekmouth swirled. Workers for the Lawes Chemical and Fertiliser Company emerged from rows of cottages attempting to stuff items into his pockets. The Bluebird and The Yellow Peril aircrafts of the Handley Page Factory hovered above, between the rough marshland of Barking Creek and the north bank of the Thames leaving white trails in the sky. Children ran from the school, mouths turning to dust as their cries faded. Debris of old lives tumbled through the nearby tidal barrier. The sound of ships sinking filled his ears. An ache in his hands intensified. Laughter from Romanian weddings rang at the entrance of The River Restaurant. He almost entered to search for hands he could borrow. He stood in the midst of it all listening, to marshy land rising, urged by the echoes of the Thames, to the sound of a great flood coming. He did not notice his feet were bleeding. His teeth began to chatter, his tongue distended. The tongue in his pocket started talking.

The last Dom, Dom Mendel stood on the bank of the river Roding, disrobing to reveal breasts jutting, her nipples hardening in the cold. Pregnant with another bloody season, her new name carved on her stomach from a serrated knife read: Filamo. She had left behind the abbey in the chasm; its entrances spitting Bible sheets, its lines leaning against a distant prayer, the faces of saints morphing into bruises. A different transformation was occurring; malevolent cherubs chased the cockerel, the limping cockerel drunk from holy water chased the Jesus figurine, squawking 'Amen!' Rolling jabuticaba fruit chased the hatched monk's fingers. And the abbey chased new burial ground. Dom Filamo listened to the symphony of cars, human traffic, the beauty of noise. She dipped her left foot into the water. After fishing a hammer and tongue from her robe pockets, she started to bludgeon her head, hitting the ring of hair. As another yolk broke and blood ran down her face, she slipped the tongue into her mouth howling. The tongue of a saint. That first kill. The reason for the punishment of a period of silence. Her skin mottled. She leapt into the river gripping the hammer, chasing the sheep's head that had surely become a different animal by now.

It's hard to write a straight story

Irenosen Okojie on Filamo

Irenosen Okojie is a Nigerian British writer. Her short-story collection Speak Gigantular *was shortlisted for the 2017 Edge Hill Short Story Prize and the Jhalak Prize.*

In this interview, Irenosen talks about her use of a concrete and familiar starting point, how she followed her instinct for tension and image, as well as the joy of writing something only loosely planned.

I read in an interview that you have always wanted to write about monks. Why is this?

I've always wanted to write about monks because physically they stand out and look so different to everyone else. It's their attire and how they carry themselves, as well as the discipline and sacrifice they have to make in their lives and their dedication to their practice – the form of their religion. All of that sparked a curiosity about the way they live. Their secret life intrigued me; that level of dedication is not easy, it costs something.

You've said 'writing is a process of investigation. If you keep yourself open, and you do the work, the joy of the craft shows on the page. You gain so much more.' As you were writing

It's hard to write a straight story

'Filamo' what do you remember being the main 'work' in realising it? How much of a joy was crafting it? What was the gain?

Writing 'Filamo' was a leap of imagination and an act of faith. I was living in East London at the time I wrote it, and every day for years I would walk past the ruins of an abbey. I found it to be a fascinating space. Creating a story set there intrigued me, I liked this idea of building it or crafting it from the ground up. That was the interest – the mystery of making that happen.

It was a joy crafting it because in some way I was giving myself permission to explore another life, another world and that sort of thing fuels me. It was a highly creative process that's also a highly mysterious process. You don't really know that world that well, so, not only do you have to research it, you also have to take that leap of faith and believe you can realise that world.

I believe that was the gain – to be able to conjure this space and these characters and this premise and make it come together in a way that worked beautifully and hopefully was interesting for the reader.

I think in some ways it's an unexpected story which I'm always keen to do. I think when people look at narratives especially from people of colour, and black people in particular, they expect certain stories. I don't think this story was expected from me so it was a joy to come from leftfield and hopefully create something that gives the reader a very exciting and enriching experience.

I hope when the reader reads the story they are picking up my excitement as a writer. If I'm excited about what I am creating on the page I think that shows in the work. That's the gain for me, the excitement, the joy and creativity as well as the hope that the reader is also absorbing those elements.

You've spoken about innovation being a response to

navigating the world as a black woman. In what way do you think surrealism is useful for exploring the world?

I am fascinated by the everyday and the surreal. I see the surreal just walking around. I think everyone has their own particular, unique way of looking at the world. I am always trying to find the poetic, the strange and the otherworldly. I think surrealism is great because it lends itself well to the kind of worlds I want to create and the kind of spaces I want to draw the reader into.

I find it hard to write a straight story, in fact I can't do it. It always goes off-kilter in some way and so I just embrace it. I think this style is something that fits well with the sort of stories and the kinds of leaps of imagination I want to take.

Marrying the everyday and the surreal gives me the permission to produce these highly imaginative fantastical worlds.

However, in places, you also use standard narrative conventions, like foreshadowing and setting. How did you balance the innovative with the conventional?

As with most stories, you feel your way through it by instinct. As a writer you are playing around and seeing what works. It's like a puzzle – you create a story bit by bit. Language choices are a balancing act – and within this is how you balance the standard and the slightly experimental.

I'm really driven to write works that take the reader elsewhere, works that challenge them and challenge myself and I think the innovative allows you to do this.

It became clear to me this was the angle I wanted to take with this story and I just ran with it and didn't stop until I'd got a first draft down.

It's a mysterious magic how you create the right balance for you. Feeling your way through it means opening yourself up to possibilities, not shutting things off.

It's hard to write a straight story

This is something I really like to do. I find that when I keep myself fluid and open, it allows for the possibility of innovation.

I don't have rigid ideas about what I want to do when I come to the page. I have only a rough idea and then I just want to keep things as open as possible so that I can create interesting textures and worlds.

In a conventional story I imagine the author forming a narrative from a static and whole structure. However, in 'Filamo' how far did your ideas and images decide the events? Was it hard keeping a sense of what had happened in order to 'build on' the story?

Like I said, I am a really instinctive writer and I think a lot of the trajectory comes from certain images I had in my head that I really wanted to get on the page – I felt these would create a really interesting trajectory, so it wasn't hard, funnily enough it was a joy.

I know this probably sounds strange because it's quite a dense story and it might have been hard for people to get a sense of what's happening, but I knew what was going to happen in my mind.

I guess the tricky thing was creating the bits in the middle and tying it all together, but I went on instinct. I think I had two weeks to write it from the time I came to the page. This always happens to me – when I get commissioned to do stuff I'll get to the stage when there's only a week to go or even less and because I'm under a certain pressure I *have* to get the story out, so it *has* to work in some way. It's not always good practice but somehow it works.

'Filamo a cloaked figure, a betrayer amongst the monks...'
Why a monk-murdering protagonist? When you first envisaged the story, was Filamo a later addition to the abbey setting or the original source of tension in the story?

The monk was always the original source of tension because I thought it was a great idea to have that sort of protagonist in that setting.

I wanted to explore what made that character get to that point and how I could make that mysterious. I wanted to find out how you create tension around that without giving context.

The monks, and Filamo in particular, were always really key to the whole story. I was operating from him as a central figure driving the story and also the reason behind why this was happening – why this world was collapsing around them. The context and the secrecy behind the violent acts, it was all tied to that monk.

What helped decide the direction this story took? Was it a conscious purpose and set of success criteria or an unconscious exploration of what 'felt right'?

It was definitely the latter, an unconscious exploration of what felt right.

The idea for the story was a response to the premise for the anthology *The Unreliable Guide to London* [published by Influx press].

The story had to be about place but how you did that was up to the writer. I had the freedom to play and just have fun and create this story.

For me it was really unconscious – the story was just a space to realise this slightly weird and wacky place.

By setting it in the ruins of an old abbey near where I lived, it gave the piece a duality because what exists there at the moment is just ruins and what I created is the whole world within it.

I found this had a real power to it – I was creating, manifesting this whole world and by the end it felt right.

That was the big reward. In the beginning the idea really excited me but I didn't know how I was going to do it. For me that is the great thing about writing. It is a process of investigation. If you come to the page knowing or thinking you know everything, I don't think it's as rewarding an experience as if you come to the page only with a loose idea of what you want to do – maybe investigate a theme or an idea – it makes it so much more exciting for you as the writer; I think that's why my stories feel so charged, that's why they have a real sense of drive and urgency and why they're so strange.

It came from my curiosity and my desire to explore the interior and exterior lives of these characters. I found it a wonderful exploration because I loved the freedom of it.

You praise Toni Morrison for her 'vividness and control' – how would you describe the control you exert?

I think I'm a very dense writer, which you can see in 'Filamo'; I think it's highly imaginative and highly creative.

The control comes when I start to do a second or third draft. In the first draft of any story I write I don't really try to have control. I think I try to do the opposite. The writing is wild actually and I'm happy about that.

In the short form where you have many restrictions it's an interesting contrast to write in this wild way. One may say you're not supposed to do that in short stories but I guess it's pushing the boundaries of what the form can do.

I am driven by how I can bend the form, how I can make it malleable, how can I make it do different things, make it interesting. So, for me the control doesn't come until later drafts, when I look at the stories again.

When I write, I tend to give myself complete freedom and enjoy the wildness because you're really just getting things out. It's almost like a skeleton.

Of course, with Morrison she's also a detailed and dense writer but she does have that control, that balance of having work that's really rich that is really strong craft-wise as well.

Even when I feel like things are hurtling in a certain direction,

I don't necessarily have that control. What this does is hopefully invigorating and challenging the reader and their expectations around particular characters and certain contexts.

Every time I come back to 'Filamo', I come back to it with a sense of joy and reward that this story was able to be realised. It just shows that as a writer you have to trust that you can create the visions you see in your mind's eye, and you can just build it bit by bit. It is a piece I'm really proud of – I really enjoyed the writing process around it.

The Flier

by Joseph O'Neill

The whole business led my wife to suggest a conference with our dear friends Pam and Becky, who were discreet and worldly and kind. She wrote them:

> Hey wonderful people! Can we drag you over for dinner Wednesday? Short notice – but there's something we'd like to talk over with you.

I prepared the meal – cucumber soup, grilled chicken breast, and a lentil-and-scallion salad. Cooking had been Viki's thing, not mine, but I'd been stuck at home for months and the kitchen had become a place of recreation. Also, my relationship with my body had changed.

Pam and Becky arrived on the dot, at seven. My illness had made me very small and very light, and they embraced me gently. 'He looks so young,' Becky said to Viki. 'Where's Molly?'

Our daughter, Molly, aged five, was spending the evening with Viki's sister, Maya. Maya and Molly didn't know what was going on. Nobody knew, not even my physician.

I poured everyone a drink – purified water, in my case – and without further ado Viki announced, 'Something strange has happened.' This was planned. Viki is an inarguably sane and well-balanced person with no history of hoaxing or chain-yanking. She is the perfect person to break unfathomable news. It's not that I've ever been the class clown, but my physical weakness had for some reason lessened my authority. 'This is all supersensitive and confidential,' Viki said.

'Uh-oh,' Becky said.

'If we're going to have a top-secret discussion, I'm going to sit down,' Pam said.

We joined her at the table. My wife said, 'I don't know how else to put this.' She moved her hand in my direction. 'He's developed the ability to fly.'

Our friends fell into a silence of incomprehension and alarm – as if we'd announced a religious conversion. Then Pam did a short laugh and said, 'Fly how?'

'As in fly like a bird,' Viki said. 'Fly.'

' "Bird," ' I said, 'is maybe taking it too far.'

'I don't get it,' Becky said.

At Viki's signal, I fetched my laptop. Everyone turned toward the screen. I played the nine-second clip that Viki had filmed with her phone.

'Let's see that again,' Pam said.

We all watched it twice more. Both times it showed the same thing: me levitating in that very room and then sort of scooting from the kitchen to the windows of our eleventh-floor apartment with my arms defensively stretched out ahead of me. I reach up with one hand and touch the ceiling. The clip ends.

Pam said, 'It's so, it's so – lifelike.'

Becky said, 'You know what it reminds me of? Mary Poppins.'

They didn't believe, or understand, their eyes. Again, we had anticipated this. Viki gave me a little kiss of encouragement, because she knew that I was about to do something I found loathsome and embarrassing.

I pushed off with my toes and floated over to the aforementioned windows. It was a clear February night. Through the panes you saw the purposeless, dominating brilliance of the skyscrapers of New York.

When I came down, our guests were looking at each other with horror. Becky's hands covered her mouth.

Viki said, 'We can't explain it, either. We can only think that it's connected to his illness.' She said, 'Are we ready for some soup?'

The soup went down well. We learned about Becky and Pam's trip to Maine, and Viki reciprocated with an update about Molly and her adventures in kindergarten. There had been issues with a boy named Andy, but Andy was now socialising more successfully.

This exchange did not involve me speaking or being spoken to. When I say that Pam and Becky were our dear friends, I really mean that they were Viki's dear friends. They were attached to me because I was attached to Viki.

I brought out the lentil salad. Becky picked up her fork, then abruptly stood up. 'This is too much for me right now,' she said. 'I'm so sorry.'

As our guests made their way out, Pam took Viki to one side and said, 'He's going to need insurance. I'll e-mail you.'

My volatility had become apparent three weeks earlier. On an errand to buy hydrogen peroxide to clean the bathroom grout, I sprang over a pool of melted snow – and rocketed to the far sidewalk, passing in front of a car that was making a turn from York Avenue. I nearly got somebody killed. I immediately returned home, treading very slowly and very softly. After I'd sat down for a while, trying to calm myself, I decided to take an experimental little leap. I hit the ceiling.

The next two days I spent mostly in bed, too consternated to move. Luckily my presence was nowhere expected. Eventually I convinced myself that I'd experienced a powerful hallucination

– a side effect of the medication I was taking, no doubt – and I decided to step out and complete my mission of buying grout cleaner. To be on the safe side, I first hopped on one foot. I took off.

There was no way around it: I'd undergone a transition, or translation. I wasn't dreaming – although it so happened that in my dreams I never flew. I didn't say anything to Viki right away. The relevant confession took place only the following week, after I'd spent some time familiarising myself with certain parameters of my new state (getting airborne; hovering; landing). My kind of aerial motion felt like sideways falling: it was scary, slightly nauseating, and unpleasant, even after I'd worked out that, by a simple but mysterious exercise of volition, I could adjust my speed and elevation. It always felt unnatural and lonely to be up in the air.

One evening, when Molly was asleep, I overcame my dread and my shame, and I sat Viki down and tried to relate what had happened to me. Of course, it took a physical demonstration to bring the facts home to her. Language alone could not effectively represent a state of affairs contradicted by physics, biology, and the history of reality. Neither of us knew what to do about it, in the sense of how to cure me. There was no discussion of what use, if any, to make of my new potentiality. 'I think we should talk it over with someone,' Viki said. 'Maybe Pam and Becky.' All in all, it was extraordinary how quickly my wife adapted. I'd say that within ten minutes of hearing, or seeing, my epochal news she was asking me what else had happened that day.

'I'm finally done,' I told her, referring to a project that had been plaguing me. I produced communications materials for a financial group. I'd foolishly got involved in drafting the annual report, which wasn't something you could just wing, given the legal framework. Being away from the office, on account of my undiagnosable ailment, hadn't made it any easier. The substance of the job was handling various stupidities, my own included.

The Flier

I was at that time a stupidist, and probably still am. Stupidism is the theory that people are stupid in the measure of their most powerful agency. They're stupid precisely when we need them not to be stupid. Much as I didn't want to be a stupidist – it's dispiriting, for starters – I recognised that it improved my grasp on things. Whereas I used to listen with great respect to what the Treasury Secretary or the C.E.O. of a booming conglomerate or even your regular talking head had to say, now I presumed that they were full of it. It was revelatory. The world makes a lot more sense when you accept that it's run by dingbats. And once you've recognised the nature of stupidity – that it expresses a relation between a person and that person's situation; that it describes the gap between what ought to be understood and done and what is, in fact, understood and done – you begin to recognise the magnitude of the problem. Stupidity isn't inevitable or constant, of course, but in the long run it almost always prevails. Alan Greenspan? Stupid, ultimately. Barack Obama? Not as smart as he needed to be, at the end of the day. Joe Schmo? Amazingly stupid.

The subject had a very personal relevance. There was something downright stupid about a flying human being. I felt, above all, stupid.

With this organising principle in my mind – not to be stupid – I followed up on Pam's suggestion about insurance. She put me on to a friend of hers, Naomi Patel, who had one of those cute little offices in the Empire State Building. Naomi, according to Pam, specialised in boutique perils. I made an appointment. Viki said doubtfully, 'I guess that makes sense.'

It was my first excursion since that fateful near-miss on York Avenue. Viki, who had left work early, held my hand as we walked to and from the taxi. She did this in order to keep me anchored to the ground as well as to convey love.

Naomi Patel was our age – late-ish thirties – and had a very reassuring and competent manner. Her office was on the seventy-sixth floor and offered a view of a silvery and gleaming

Hudson River and a silvery and gleaming New York Harbor. I cleaned my glasses to get a better look, because it was that order of spectacle – the order that reminds you of words like 'argentine' and 'numinous.'

She listened conscientiously, making notes on a yellow pad. When I'd finished, she put down her pen and removed her glasses and said, to Viki, 'Have I understood this correctly? Your husband' – a little ironically, it seemed to me, she checked her notes – 'has the power of flight?'

'Um, yes,' Viki said. She was making the face that we'd agreed she would make, namely, a face signalling to the insurance broker that she should humor the eccentric husband. We didn't want the broker to believe that I was truly an aeronaut.

Naomi Patel said, 'That is unusual.' She continued, 'I've handled a lot of dangerous activities – skydiving, wingsuit flying, really far-out stuff – but never this. Huh.'

She reflected for a moment, calculating whether my case would produce a commission and how much work it would involve. You could practically see her brow and mouth creasing into plus and minus and equals signs. Or she was thinking how best to get me out of her office. She said decisively, 'You need to think of yourself as a car, or a helicopter. You're going to need protection against accidental damage to yourself – it's called A. D. & D., and covers death or dismemberment – and you need liability insurance, in case you cause loss to others. The tricky piece is assessing the risk. We're going to have to give the underwriters some guidance.' She swivelled to her keyboard. 'I'm sending you the application form.'

It seems that nothing can proceed, at a certain point in life, without filling out a form – without boring a new hole in one's small bowl of time.

That's O.K. The older I get, the greater grows my respect for the underground deeds that make our lives persistently functional. Nobody told me, growing up, that in addition to a regular career one must embrace a secret administrative vocation. I can hardly believe that for years I lived in a fantastical world in which I gave no thought to ventilation solutions, health-provision networks, wood conditioner, bylaws, credit scores, automatic-payment dates, storage space, and propane.

When we got home, I ate some chocolate-peanut-butter ice cream, for the calories, then made use of the bathroom, then retreated to bed in order to fill out the insurance questionnaire. Viki and Molly were in the living room, cutting paper with tiny yellow scissors.

> Please describe the activity for which you seek insurance coverage, specifying the scope of the activity, including frequency, locations, safety measures. State any relevant experience or qualifications.

The assumption, here, was that I would zip around of my own free will. But why on earth would I do that? Who knew how long I could stay aloft? What about the wind, rain, lightning, radiation, and cold? What would I wear? What about my glasses? What about drones and aircraft and wind turbines and electrical wires and chimneys and miscellaneous poles? Any sizable city would be a death trap, basically. As for the countryside, everyone out there was locked and loaded. Anything that moved in the sky they shot. They gunned down ducks and turkeys by the million. I'd have to fly at night, like an owl. No: I needed insurance only for involuntary or emergency flights. Who knew what lay ahead? I might fall out of an airplane. I might find myself caught in a fire or fleeing rising waters. Even then, even in extremis, I would fly only as a last resort. There were systems in place. The parachute had been invented. We had fire exits and flood alerts and evacuation plans. We had disaster preparedness. The great fray, in the real world, wasn't good versus evil. It was perils versus protocols.

From the bedroom doorway I said, 'Hey, Molly. What would you do if you could fly?'

Molly stayed focussed on her work. Even a five-year-old could see that the question was absurd. She said, 'I would fly to pasta.'

I said, 'What else?' I was convinced that she knew something that I could not know.

'I would fly to you,' Molly said, to her mother.

A day or two later, there was a meeting at the office. The purpose of the meeting was to review the draft annual report. My bodily presence was required, and the C.C.O. himself was also going to be there. I was excited. It had been a long time since I'd gone in. I got dressed up. My one belt, I discovered, was now too long for me, and like a teen-ager I had to punch an extra hole in the strap to accommodate the prong. Viki said, 'Why don't you put on your blue sweater? It makes you look taller. I can't explain it, it makes you taller.'

The meeting went well. 'I have no idea what "agile feedback loops" means,' the C.C.O. said. 'I like it.' Everyone laughed. I waited for somebody to credit me with the phrase, but no one did. In fact, and I guess to my relief, I wasn't mentioned or called on at all.

Afterward I accompanied Valerie Acevedo and Alexis Chen, who were workplace buddies and funny, to the smoking balcony. I didn't smoke, but to hightail it home right after the meeting would risk giving the wrong impression. This balcony was on the thirty-second floor and had snow on it. The daylight was fading. Across the street, a lustrous tower was filled with white-shirted workers.

'What this place needs,' Alexis said, vaping, 'is Acapulco chairs.'

'Which ones are they?' Valerie said.

'You know – with the bouncy vinyl cords. They're made for the outdoors. Hence "Acapulco." '

I started laughing. 'Wait – "Hence Acapulco"?'

Alexis continued, 'Well, how did last night go?'

'Fun. Good,' Valerie said evenly.

Alexis made a listening noise.

Valerie, suddenly inspired, said, 'It's like I'm like a restaurant. Like he liked me like he'd like a restaurant. Like, "That was cool. I should come here again." '

Alexis said quickly, ' "The osso buco was excellent." '

They both laughed and drew on their e-cigarettes. I made a proximate sound, but quietly. I didn't feel like a party to the conversation; I felt merely privy to it. It surprised me that they were talking about this stuff, because I thought a masculine presence would be inhibitive. Maybe corporate-banter norms had changed in my absence.

Alexis said, 'And?'

Valerie said, 'Yeah, it was sweet. He was kind of . . . focussed on the details. On trend. What's that word? Artisanal.'

Alexis said, 'Yeah, the craft-brewer thing. Expert but traditional. I'm on the fence.'

Valerie waited a beat, like an actual comedian, then said, very dryly, 'Still, it's been a while since I saw penis.' The two women laughed explosively.

It was at this moment that I did something stupid. I put my weight on my heels and, from my position next to them, rose about three feet off the floor and floated backward into the building. I watched them for a moment. They were talking and vaping as before. They had failed to notice – I say this in all objectivity – one of the most wondrous occurrences in the history of humankind.

When I got home, Pam was sitting at the table. She had not removed her coat. Viki was on the sofa with Molly, fixing her up with headphones and an iPad. That wasn't normally permitted on weekdays. Something was up.

I decided to make green tea.

I overheard Pam telling Viki that Becky had physically attacked her; that it wasn't the first time this had happened; that on this occasion Pam had felt in mortal danger. 'I'm scared she's going to come by here,' she said.

'This is terrible,' Viki said. She was wringing her hands, which wasn't like her. But the situation was unusually vexing. Her primary allegiance was to Becky, not to Pam. Viki had known Pam only since the moment, about five years before, when she had surfaced as Becky's first girlfriend. Viki's friendship with Becky went back to their undergrad days at Boston College, where they belonged to a Thomas Aquinas study group whose members had stayed in touch, more or less, ever since – 'the old theology gang,' Viki called them.

The first time I met Viki, I asked her what theology was, exactly. She answered that it was the study of the nature of the divine. She must have known that this was a very, very hot thing to say, particularly to someone like me, an atheist and a desperado. When I asked if she believed in God, she murmured, also hotly, 'Would that I did.' For years the subject didn't come up again. Then, one night, when I was beset by anguish at my deformation, I confided to Viki in the darkness of our bedroom that I felt overwhelmingly confused. 'I just don't understand it,' I said.

There was a pause. From out of the dark her voice said, 'The ultimate end of man is to understand God, in some fashion.'

'I'm sorry?'

The Viki voice whispered, 'All things exist in order to attain the divine likeness.'

A third voice sounded: Molly had woken up with a shout of fear. We heard the rapidly thumping approach of a panicked little sprinter. The door crashed open, and then she was in bed with us, and then she was asleep in the space between her mother and father.

Pam wasn't part of the old theology gang. Pam was out of

The Flier

Peru, New York. When Becky had begun furtively dating her, she had referred to her as the Peruvian. Becky had always been straight, and Viki and I thought the Peruvian was a dude from the Andes. It was quite the thunderbolt when we were introduced to a woman, somewhat older and beefier than any of us, who worked as a purchasing manager in Long Island City. We liked Pam right away. She was warm and lively and had all these stories about hunting ghosts on Valcour Island and making out with Vermont girls on the banks of the Ausable River. In all honesty, we soon preferred her company to Becky's, not that anyone was making comparisons.

And yet, even if Pam was more fun, she was more detachable. It would have been easier for Viki if it had been Pam, not Becky, who was the one doing the beating up.

I served Viki and Pam the green tea. I don't know why, but it bothered me that Pam hadn't removed her coat. It added to the disturbance.

Pam related that she'd started a breakup discussion – not for the first time – and Becky had flown into a rage. She started throwing things, including a glass paperweight that if it had hit Pam on the head would have brained her.

I had been in Pam and Becky's apartment many times. It was full of tchotchkes. If you wanted to throw things, there was no shortage of ammunition.

'Oh, my God,' Viki said.

'She went to look for my gun,' Pam said. 'She knows I keep it in one of the shoeboxes. She had this look on her face. She wanted to stop me from leaving. I ran out before she could get me.'

'Oh, my God,' Viki said.

Pam showed us her phone. There were twenty-seven missed calls from Becky.

I was in the kitchen, throwing together some dinner. 'You can get a restraining order,' I said. 'There are things that can be done.'

Pam seemed not to hear. Viki was looking at Molly. Molly, still wearing headphones, was grinning and squirming as she interacted with her iPad.

The buzzer sounded.

Viki said, 'Are we expecting a delivery?'

That was my province – online grocery shopping. 'No,' I said. Nobody moved. We listened.

The buzzer sounded again.

'It's her,' Pam said. 'I'm telling you, it's her.'

I turned off the gas flame and put a lid on the saucepan. I wiped my hands with a dishcloth. Dinner was pretty much ready. The kale had been steamed and the chickpeas and onions had been sautéed.

'That's strange,' Viki said, peering at the intercom video. 'I don't see anyone.'

I went over to see for myself. Nobody was visible at the entrance.

Viki said, 'She might be inside already. Someone might have let her in.'

Our building had no doorman. In order to enter, a visitor had to be buzzed through two doors. However, if the visit coincided with a person exiting the building, often the doors would be held open as a courtesy. This didn't mean that the visitor could go right up, however, because the elevator was controlled by the host.

The intercom screen went dark, which was to be expected.

I said, 'Look, it might not be her.' It happened sometimes – an impatient food-delivery guy buzzing multiple apartments.

Viki said, 'She just texted me.'

Bring me up? In the elevator.

Our front door has two locks. I turned them both.

Viki said, 'Let me talk to her.'

I got out three plates and served the food.

Viki made the call from the bedroom. We didn't speak, Pam and I. I thought about putting an arm around her, but was deterred by the bulk of her coat. She didn't touch her food.

Viki came out of the bedroom. She sat down at the table. Her face was exhausted or something. She said slowly, 'She won't leave. "I want to talk to her," she keeps saying, in this weird calm voice. "I have a right to talk to her." She sounds off. She sounds really off.'

'Maybe we're jumping to conclusions here,' I said.

'That stupid gun,' Pam said. 'I'm scared, Vik.'

Viki said to nobody in particular, 'She wanted to be a missionary. In college. You know – go to Africa. Convert everyone.'

Pam started crying. She displayed her phone: the calls were still coming.

I didn't know if Pam's assessment of the threat was reliable or not, but I did know that very specific situations are associated with murder and mayhem, and that a breakup is one such situation. I said, 'There's no way out of the building except through the lobby. We're going to have to call the cops.'

'No,' Pam said, her face in her hands. 'They'll shoot her. No.'

I was filling my mouth with kale when I noticed that Pam was pointing a finger at me. 'You,' she said. 'You could do something. You know what I'm talking about.'

Viki was contemplating me with a strange expression. 'Yes,' she said. 'Yes. I forgot all about that. My God, yes.'

I took a sip of green tea. The important thing was not to do anything dumb.

As I was deliberating, as I was trying to determine exactly how an uninsured aerial intervention would help matters, I was blindsided by a feeling that I can describe only as a powerful sense of arrival – as if all my life I had been trekking, in a series of unconscious gradations and unconscious turns, on an imperceptible road that finally, at this exact moment, had delivered me to a new place and a new dimension of action.

Slowly, I stood up. I went to a window and opened it. Bright, enigmatic apartments were everywhere. As the cold entered the room, I turned toward the two women so that they could behold my face. I spread my arms as if they were wings. I rose into the air. 'Tell me what I should do,' I said, and their visages filled with awe and dread.

Viki's sister, Maya, is in the habit of dropping by without warning. In mitigation, she has a recognisable, superfluously insistent way of buzzing that functions as a heads-up. I was still aloft by the window, my back to the flaming skyscrapers, when her specific buzz sounded. Viki immediately said, 'Maya?'

I glided to the intercom. There she was, humorously blowing a cloud of breath and cigarette smoke into the door camera. Before I could react, she was looking through the glass front doors and waving at someone inside. That person had to be Becky, whom Maya had known for years. Maya was let into the building.

Viki said with sudden conviction, 'Maya will handle her.'

I knew Maya to be a good-hearted if somewhat erratic person. She had a history of eccentric and disastrous sales ventures that she ran out of her basement apartment in the East Village. She owned a harp that she couldn't play. She had opinions about yogurts and blue algae and the energies of rooms. It was all a bit silly, to my mind, but it was Maya who had astonishingly observed to Viki, 'There's something different about him. I don't know what it is. But his energy has definitely changed.'

Who am I to scoff at extrasensory perception? Who am I to rule out the idea of a supernature? It was precisely Maya's heightened atmospheric instincts that led her to detect (she later reported) a 'funky aura' about Becky that night. Maya stated that she'd long had this funny feeling about Becky, who was 'always sort of shrinking herself for no reason' and for this reason had to be 'bottling up a lot of negativity and anger.' When she saw Becky loitering in the lobby, she knew straightaway that something was very wrong. 'It was her ponytail,' Maya said. 'It was so neat and vicious. She's, like, 'What a coincidence, I just got here,' and in my head I'm, like, Learn how to lie, lady.'

Maya and Becky entered the elevator. They stood inside the brushed-steel box for a minute or two. 'I guess they're not in,' Maya suggested.

'Oh, they're in,' Becky said. 'Pam told me to come. They're just not letting us up for some reason. I'm worried. I think there might be an emergency. I called them earlier, but got no response. We have to find a way up there.'

Maya said, 'I'm going to text them. If we don't hear back quickly, I'll start to worry.' They left the elevator and sat down on the lobby bench.

Maya's text to Viki read:

Call 911. I've got this.

How did Maya understand the situation so swiftly and so correctly, without any of the facts? How did she see through Becky and her plausible story? How could she have been so smart?

Viki always does as her big sister says. She called 911.

About six minutes later, the red and white lights of squad cars were flashing in the street. Maya opened the door to twelve cops from the Nineteenth Precinct. They identified Becky and arrested her on the spot, evidently a compulsory procedure in domestic-violence cases. Becky went very quietly, like a little lamb, Maya said, just as Maya had figured she would.

Two of the cops, a woman and a man, came up with Maya. We all sat down. Maya said, 'You found a weapon on her, right? I sensed a weapon.'

'I'll come to that,' the woman police officer said.

Later it became known that Maya was right. Becky had been carrying Pam's gun.

The woman police officer separately interviewed Viki and Pam and Maya. There was a lot of paperwork; everything was methodically written down. I wasn't asked to make a statement. I hung out with Molly, who was interested in what was going on and kept trying to remove her headphones. The woman police officer explained to Pam what her options were, and recommended a 'safety plan.' Pam said, 'She's dangerous. I want to emphasise that she's dangerous. I don't want to see her again.' The woman police officer repeated to Pam what remedies were available to her and what systems were in place to protect her. She gave Pam three brochures, which Viki and I leafed through, because our friend was in no state to retain information. The N.Y.P.D., I read, annually processes more than two hundred thousand domestic-violence calls. Pam, coat and all, went to hug the woman police officer. The officer accepted this with professionalism. She had been trained to handle hugs, too.

The thing that struck me was how orderly these cops were. It made me feel hopeful.

It was agreed that Pam would spend the night in a hotel a couple of blocks away and that Viki would walk her there. Maya went home.

Amazingly, Molly was still awake. She sat on the living-room floor surrounded by animal figurines and other objects. The big cats, her favorites, were arranged in a long line. There was a group of unicorns. There were green soldiers and there were glass beads and there were bears and there was at least one crocodile. A dinosaur, massively bigger than the other toys, lay on its side. Molly has very white skin and dark-brown hair. She was murmuring as she manipulated the creatures, and I tried in vain, from my chair, to make out what the creatures were saying to one another. Some kind of drama of cooperation seemed to be taking place. There was an imaginary obstacle, a crevasse or a river, and the animals were helping one another across. Then a battle started. A soldier battled a shark, who battled a unicorn, who defeated the shark, who reattacked. When the white tiger was imperilled by the lynx, some turtles and sheep flew to the tiger's aid. One by one the combatants were downed, then picked up and revived by a girl's giant hand. Would that, Molly seemed to be repeating. Would that.

She yawned.

'Let's go to bed,' I said. I took her hand. 'It'll all be here in the morning.'

This was nearly two thousand mornings ago. Within weeks, I lost the power to fly, if that's what the power was. My theory is that I regained weight and became too heavy, but who knows. I never again discussed this strange chapter with anyone, not even with Viki, and increasingly I find myself unsure that it happened. The video clip of my airborne self has been lost. But I have my confirmation. Molly's toys are stored in a box under her bed, where they can easily be found. Once or twice a year she'll wistfully resurrect them, the white tiger and his gang, and I see with my own eyes that there was once a flier.

You don't want
to see it coming

Joseph O'Neill on The Flier

*Joseph O'Neill is an Irish novelist and non-fiction writer.
His novel* Netherland *was awarded the 2009 PEN/
Faulkner Award for Fiction and the Kerry Group Irish
Fiction Award. This story is one of several of his that
have appeared in* The New Yorker.

*In our interview, we talked about how he had
written a story that seemed to veer from its expected
path, about his original intention for the story and the
importance of the writer not knowing too much.*

**The protagonist seems to contain a variety of contrary
characteristics. He is at times nervous and mild, but also
pretty boastful about his flying skills. What do you think of
him?**

I'm not sure what to think of him. He's a kind of urban
everyman, maybe, the contemporary version of the man in the
grey flannel suit, with a familiar set of anxieties and well-hidden
dreams.

**You have said: 'The elevation of fantasy as a way of
investigating the human experience has been taken to an**

embarrassing extreme.' How did you find writing something fantastical in a fictional world otherwise so realistic?

I was intent on taking a really big – I'd even say weirdly big – motif of popular culture, the superhero, and almost running the numbers on it through the lens of realism. I wrote this story pretty quickly, once I'd had the basic idea (which came to me while doing a road trip). The hard part wasn't so much imagining what it would be like if someone like yours truly could suddenly fly, but connecting the lurid dimensions – wow, I can fly, amazing – to what they used to call the human condition.

Is this story about gender? Was it a response to something in particular?

I suppose I reached the point when I was taken aback by just how powerful the idea of a supernaturally strong or gravity-defying protagonist had become in the minds not only of children but of adults – and how it was taken for granted that such powers would be deployed in the fight of good against evil, and how, in the great majority of cases, the superpower is put to good use. This involves a fantasy of escape from the basic terms of life, the binding and sometimes onerous contracts of living with others in a society. The dream of unlimited or enhanced agency is particularly appropriate to groups who, in real life, experience their agency in limited, even unjust terms. A lot of women fall into that category, of course. Simultaneously, there seem to be a lot of men running around who have enormous anxiety about their loss of gendered power. It has enormous, destructive political consequences, and is something that interests me. So in answer to your first question: Yes. In part.

The scene where Becky comes to the apartment misfoots any reader expecting a conventional climax. Was this an early plan of yours or did it come about as you wrote it?

I didn't see it coming either. You don't want to see it coming, if you're the writer. Because if you don't, neither will the reader.

There is much implied and left unsaid in this story. Do you cut back on this information as you edit or can you calibrate how much info to give as you write?

I try to leave as much out as I possibly can. Life is mysterious, and a story can partake of that mystery.

A number of themes recur in the story – is their recurrence something you planned or something you found yourself doing unconsciously?

Their recurring was unconscious! I wasn't aware of it until you asked me about it. That's great. The story should know something that you, the writer, don't know.

When you describe New York, you don't seem to want a conventional sense of 'realism' – what was your intention with your descriptions of setting?

Can I disagree? New York, certainly the bit of it where I live, truly can be a Gothic city, with vast verticals of checkered light and humans toiling and seething within, and dragons of money breathing fire in the dark.

Was it essential to this story that it was funny?

I can't help myself. It's how I see the world. Funny is an absolute good, in my eyes. I think this is better understood in Ireland and Britain than it is in the USA. I would even suggest that the peoples of those rainy islands find it difficult to take someone seriously unless they're funny.

Acknowledgements

'Theophrastus and the Dancing Plague' by Jessie Greengrass taken from *An Account of the Decline of the Great Auk, According to One Who Saw It* ©, 2015, used by permission of John Murray Press, an imprint of Hodder and Stoughton Ltd.

'Mrs Fox' by Sarah Hall taken from *Madame Zero* © 2017, used by permission of Faber and Faber Ltd. (Worldwide excluding US).

© 2017 by Sarah Hall. Used by permission of HarperCollins Publishers (USA).

'The First Punch' by Jon McGregor first published in *Granta* © 2003, used by permission of The Wylie Agency (UK) Ltd.

'Filamo' by Irenosen Okojie taken from *Nudibranch* © 2019, used by permission of Little, Brown Book Group Ltd.

'The Flier' by Joseph O'Neill, first published in *The New Yorker* © 2019, used by permission of the author, c/o Rogers Coleridge & White Ltd., 20, Powis Mews, London, W11 1JN

'The Crossing' taken from *Mothers* by Chris Power © 2018, used by permission of Faber and Faber Ltd. (Worldwide excluding USA).

Reprinted by permission of Farrar, Straus and Giroux. All Rights Reserved (USA).

'Hair' by Mahreen Sohail, first published in *Granta* © 2020, used by permission of the author, c/o Georges Borchardt, Inc.

This project has been made possible through the kind support of Cathy Galvin, the founder and director of The Word Factory UK.